Saving the

A Be the General Manager Book

Bryant T. Jordan

Sports Seer Publishing

Saving the Lakers: A Be the General Manager Book

© Copyright 2014 by Bryant T. Jordan

Published by Sports Seer Publishing

Library and Archives Canada Cataloguing in Publication

Jordan, Bryant T., 1979-, author

   Saving the Lakers : a be the General Manager book / Bryant T. Jordan.

Issued in print and electronic formats.

ISBN 978-1-927654-23-1 (pbk.).--ISBN 978-1-927654-24-8 (bound).--

ISBN 978-1-927654-25-5 (pdf)

   1. Los Angeles Lakers (Basketball team). 2. Basketball teams--United States--Management. 3. Basketball managers--United States.I. Title.

GV885.52.L67J66 2014   796.323'640979494   C2014-902390-1

C2014-902391-X

Publisher: **www.SportsSeerPublishing.com**

Book: **www.SavingTheLakers.com**

Similar Book: **www.SavingTheCeltics.com**

Author: **www.BryantTJordan.com**

Dedicated to God: Father, Word and Holy Spirit

Also by Bryant T. Jordan

Saving the Celtics: A Be the General Manager Book
www.SavingThecCeltics.com

An Open Letter to ALL Regarding Donald Sterling
www.bryantTjordan.com/donald-sterling-book/

Everything negative - pressure, challenges –is all an opportunity for me to rise.

-Kobe Bryant

I have to tell you, I'm proudest of my life off the court. There will always be great basketball players who bounce that little round ball, but my proudest moments are affecting people's lives, effecting change, being a role model in the community.

- Magic Johnson

You can't get much done in life if you only work on the days when you feel good.

- Jerry West

ACKNOWLEDGEMENTS

First and foremost I want to thank my first love, God the Father, Word and Holy Spirit. Without Him I am nothing.

I would also like to thank the late Dr. Jerry Buss, the Logo Jerry West and Shaquille O'Neal for the summer of 96' and the amazing eight years that followed, as well as Kobe Bryant for the past 18 years (as well as for helping me purchase my first house – see the prologue to learn more). I also want to thank Dominque Wilkins, Charles Barkley, the Bad Boy Pistons and Larry Johnson and the Runnin' Rebels; you were each an inspiration to a knucklehead who could be dead or in prison if it weren't for the fact that I spent most of my waking hours either hooping or safely watching basketball games in my room, rather than runnin' around Shaqtin' a fool.

Last but certainly not least I would like to thank my magnificent wife and our precious children; words cannot express how thankful I am to have been blessed with each and every one of you and how very much I love you. May you each serve God above all and always do what you believe is right, no matter what anyone else thinks, says, or does!

CONTENTS

PROLOGUE:
How A Cocky Kid From Philly Turned A Once Die-Hard Pistons Fan Into A Lakers Fan And Bought Him A House To Boot

It was the summer of 1996 and I was seventeen years old. Basketball had been my first love for many years. I had skipped countless days of school to play pickup games at the local park, walked home from school upon learning that my favorite college team was playing an afternoon NCAA tournament game, and even skipped out on my second and third loves (video games and food) in order to play up to 10 hours a day that summer.

I had become quite good at the game I loved, perhaps not NBA level good but quite possibly good enough to earn a living playing professionally in an overseas league. I was a 6'2" (read 6'4" in NBA terms) combo guard who could pass the rock beautifully and rebound like a player 6" taller. I also had an incredibly diverse offensive repertoire that featured an adept post game and deadly range and accuracy on my jumper (I loved taking bets from jokers who didn't think I could hit insanely deep 3's on the playground). I still remember the first time I was ever asked for an autograph - I was 12 years old and had just finished scoring every single point for my team, including many extremely deep three-pointers (for those of you who remember the University of Arkansas Razorbacks' Alex Dillard, you get the idea) during a streetball tournament game victory. I felt as if the world was mine that day and Stacey Augmon himself couldn't have stopped me (unless of course Richard Perry paid him to let me score, ahem, ahem).

Of course I was also a loose cannon that never got along with my coaches, talked a great deal of trash to opposing players, berated my own teammates for doing anything other than passing me the ball and stopped playing anything but street tournaments and blacktop games of 1-on-1 and the like long before I graduated from high school. In short, I was a prototypical knucklehead.

I had visions of *walking* on at the University of Nevada Las Vegas (UNLV) and while that may not have been entirely realistic (though I do believe I could have made their 1997-98 squad as a freshman and played behind New Zealand's Mark Dickel - who could really ball by the way), I have no real doubt that I could have played Division One ball *somewhere*. Alas, playing college ball was not meant to be, and thank God for that! Instead I fell in love with the woman of my dreams, repented of my sins and gave my life to the Lord and Savior Jesus Christ of Nazareth, entered the ministry (though I now consider myself a Biblical Christian rather than any particular denomination as I am still not very fond of organized religion and would rather just serve my God, obey His word, and let the chips fall where they may), became a father of nine amazing children (at the time of this writing – who knows what the future holds) and all but gave up on actually playing the game I once loved so dearly.

There was also the matter of an irregular heart-beat, flipping out of a construction truck and landing on my back, messing up both my ankles and knees as well as my back and even later not being able to walk for quite a while due to a slipped disc in my back, but honestly all of that is beside the point. God became my first love and basketball, well, basketball is still is the *game* I love more than any other!

Enough about me and my not so illustrious hoops credentials - back to the summer of 1996. That summer was a great time to be alive, a great time to be a basketball fan and an even greater time to be a Laker fan, for that summer a new NBA dynasty was created, thanks in large part to *The Logo*, Jerry West. During the summer of 96' West pulled off perhaps the single most lop sided and some would say clairvoyant trade in the history of the NBA when he convinced the Charlotte Bobcats to trade the rights to the 13th pick in the NBA Draft (a pick the Lakers used on 17 year old Kobe Bean Bryant) for Serbian center Vlade Divac.

While many people excuse the Hornets titanic blunder, believing there was no way they could have known a mere high school kid would turn out to be the second coming of Michael Jordan and one of the three best scorers (along with Jordan and the great Wilt Chamberlain) to ever step foot on a basketball court, such isn't exactly true. The truth is that Kobe Bryant was the son of former superstar collegian and very solid NBA player Joe Bryant (who averaged 21.8 points per game and 11.4 rebounds per game on .517 shooting in his final collegiate season at LaSalle), nephew of former NBA player Chubby Cox (who was drafted by the Chicago Bulls in 1978 and last played for the Washington Bullets during the 1982-83 season - and yes that really was what his friend's called him though his birth name was John Arthur Cox III), had just finished leading a once moribund high school program (Lower Merion High School) to a state title, and even crushed the aforementioned Wilt Chamberlain's Pennsylvania high school career scoring record of 2,252 points by scoring an obscene 2,883 points. The kid known as Bean had even been named both the *Naismith High School Player of the Year* and the *Gatorade Men's National Basketball Player of the Year.*

Bryant was also known to have destroyed one of the NCAA's top scorers in pre-draft work-outs, a 6'8, 220 lb. small forward and grown man by the name of Dontae Jones. Jones had just finished leading the Mississippi State Bulldogs to an SEC tournament championship (which he earned MVP honors of) and an unexpected Final Four berth after being named the Regional MVP along the way. Clearly Kobe Bean Bryant was something special.

Of course, it's also true that Vlade Divac was no slouch. Divac was known as perhaps the best passing center in the league as well as one of the best passing centers of all-time. When it became common knowledge that the Hornets had never even considered drafting Bryant before trading the rights to the pick to the Lakers, it became obvious that trading for Vlade Divac was far better than drafting one of the available center prospects in the 1996 Draft such as Efthimios Rentzias or Priest Lauderdale. However, no matter how one spins it, the Bryant for Divac trade will live in infamy and may even be regarded as the beginning of *the Kobe curse* for as long as the Hornets remain a basketball team, be they in Charlotte, New Orleans, or China one day (though if they moved to China they could be called the *Dragons,* have a great mascot and serve the best sushi of any NBA team, and that alone would be cause for celebration).

Less than one month after acquiring Bryant, Jerry West would pull off the impossible and convince the most dominant physical force the game had ever seen, Shaquille O'Neal, to leave *Disney World* and the Orlando Magic for *Disney Land* and the greatest franchise in professional sports. The Los Angeles Lakers were back, *Showtime* was back and I was pumped!

Shaquille O'Neal had been my favorite player since the first time I watched him play a game at Louisiana State University. While most kids my age, and for that matter adults my size, seemed to gravitate to the guards and perhaps wing players, there was just something about the *Shaq Attack* that I found especially awesome. Although I was a natural guard who loved to shoot deep threes, I began working on my post-up game relentlessly and the first time someone called me *baby Shaq* during a pickup game I was elated.

As Shaq was my favorite player the Orlando Magic instantly became my favorite team in the summer of 92', supplanting my beloved Detroit Pistons, a team I had grown up rooting for and had season tickets to with my mother during their *Bad Boys* years. However when Shaq was drafted by the Magic, I was a Magic man through and through.

The above said, it goes without saying that when Shaq signed with the Lakers, the Lakers would instantly become my favorite team, a near sports-blasphemy for a one-time die-hard Pistons fan. However, truth be told there was something about that cocky, smiling kid from Philly that had been drafted less than a month earlier that had already had me leaning towards becoming a die-hard Lakers fan.

Over the course of the 1996-97 season something strange happened to me. Shaquille O'Neal, the great *Shaq Attack* that had been my favorite player for around seven years had become my second favorite player. The cocky, smiling kid from Philly had won my basketball heart.

Over the next six years I read just about everything I could about Kobe Bryant and quickly felt that while I had never met him we were somehow kindred spirits. I had never felt that way about Shaq, I had simply been amazed by his power and attracted to his personality but with Kobe I literally felt as if I had a personal connection, and honestly there were some interesting similarities. Kobe and I were nearly the same age, we were both thought to be extremely intelligent but also hard-headed, we each married a woman, and at an age, that our family didn't necessarily agree with, we each had a falling out with our family that wasn't caused by any overt fault of our own, we each had a me-against-the-world mentality (I used to start my days listening to *F**k the World* by 2PAC – which honestly, even as a Christian I can still appreciate a great deal, as to be a Christian is to be in the world but not of it and therefore to have a *me-against-the-world* mentality), and of course, we were both Laker fans!

There was also a financial connection between Kobe Bryant and I, as strange as that may sound. You see, I was raised by a mother who was very wise with her money, a father who despised working for anyone but himself and a Grandmother who not only lavished me with copious financial gifts (such as giving me $250 for receiving an A on my report card when most of my friends might receive $5-10 for such, or $500 in bribe money to assure that I wouldn't play high school football when the only way my friends could make $500 was to work full-time for two weeks in the summer) but encouraged me to invest and increase the funds I was given rather than spend them on video games or clothes like most of my school age buddies did. All of this combined to make me, what I like to refer as, a *self-employed wise gambler,* and yes I know the term wise gambler sounds like an oxymoron but I was indeed a gambler and I was no moron.

I had always been interested in sports cards and sports memorabilia growing up and at one time I had some of the nicest and most valuable Shaquille O'Neal, Marshall Faulk and Drew Bledsoe collections on the planet. When Kobe Bryant came on the scene in 1996 I literally felt like I had to invest in him, just had too.

I decided to sell just about every single card and autographed jersey, ball and picture I had in my collection and use those funds, along with those I received from selling *Disney* stock and my own personal savings ($250 per A adds up pretty quick) to purchase as many Kobe Bryant *Topps Finest* rookie cards as I could get my hands on. Back then eBay wasn't very big and I had to go to local card shows almost every weekend to stock up; however after a while I had quite a stack of the gorgeous shiny bronze cards with funny peel attached called *Topps Finest*.

Had I merely held onto this stack of cards until after the Lakers 3-peat in 2002 I certainly could have turned a huge profit, however I was far too much of a gambler to just sit on such an investment. Instead I started researching ways to multiply the value of my new collection, be it through trading the cards for autographed items or even sending the cards themselves to Kobe through the mail to get autographed (generally not a good idea unless the cards you are sending are *commons* and not of significant value, or unless you enjoy losing cards, though I will say that when I wrote to Shaquille O'Neal and Tracy McGrady at one point, each player did send me an autographed item through the mail). However, what I decided to do turned out to be the best decision possible in my estimation. I had found out that the *Topps Chrome* rookie cards of Kobe, which at that time were far less valuable than the *Topps Finest* version I had a pile of, were in fact far rarer. Knowing that supply and demand is the primary factor in escalating values for items I decided straight away to trade all of my *Topps Finest* Kobe rookie cards for as many *Topps Chrome* Kobe rookie cards as I could get my hands on - and boy oh boy was I successful in doing so!

When the dust settled and I had a massive stack of the *Topps Chrome* rookie cards, which by this time were extremely coveted and selling for many times what the *Topps Finest* rookie cards were selling for, I decided that owning a home would be far more worthwhile than owning a stack of cardboard pieces with pictures on them, even if those pieces of cardboard were chrome colored and shiny and the pictures were of Kobe Bryant. Thanks to the good Lord I was able to sell that stack of sports cards and purchase my first home with my precious wife, with nothing but good ole cash money! Today I can literally and honestly say with a smile that Kobe Bryant, at least in part, bought me my first house.

INTRODUCTION

If you haven't read the *Prologue,* read it now! I didn't write it so you could ignore it, and besides, it's an interesting, enlightening and entertaining read … so, read it!

Now that my demands have been met (they better have been met … if not, go back and read the prologue before I reach through this book and slap you), it's time for yet another section in a book that the vast majority of readers seem to ignore, the *Introduction*. Read this too!

If you read the Prologue (and you better have) you probably already guessed that I was not merely a jock and hoops junkie, I was a numbers guy, stats geek and financial nerd and still am; you would be right. Ever since I was extremely young I have been a bit of a walking calculator, able to do many mathematical equations in my head faster than another can do with a calculator at his or her disposal. When I became interested in sports, it was only natural that I would instantly also become interested in player's salaries, team salary constraints and the like.

After I basically hung up my high-tops for good in order to give my ankles, knees and back a break, the financial side of the game invaded my mind even more. When websites like RealGM.com and HoopsHype.com with its team salary pages came on-line, I was in arm-chair GM heaven. I quickly memorized the salaries of perhaps over 100 players and began constructing trades in my head and on-paper to improve every team in the league. I also started writing on various websites and forums which almost always led to my being kicked off the site by some overzealous moderator or cyber-Nazi who happened to disagree with my opinions on his or her favorite team's problems and how to fix them with a trade that made both basketball and financial sense. Such is life.

No matter, when the urge to write a trade proposal crept up I simply searched the web for another website, and of course, used a separate pseudonym. I even ran my own sports blog for a short time until I realized that I just didn't have enough time to dedicate to it, with all the other family, ministry and writing projects I was involved in. However when Kobe Bryant went down with his Achilles injury and the Lakers season inevitably went down the tubes without him, I was a bit burned out. Life was happening, our ninth child was on the way, my family and I were planning a cross country relocation and I simply disappeared from the forums and websites I had once so passionately haunted.

Life is still happening and now just two months after relocating and getting all settled in we are once again planning to relocate. I suppose it could be called both a blessing and a curse to be a freelance writer and not tied down to any particular location. I prefer to look at it as a great blessing but it sure does make searching for real estate a daunting task when you have an entire country's listings to consider and sift through rather than one particular city inside one particular state of one particular country.

However, although life is still as unpredictable as ever, the NBA season is upon us yet again, the Lakers are once again the talk of the NBA, even if for all the wrong reasons (such as ESPN ranking them the 4th worst team in the Western Conference this season) and Kobe Bryant is getting ready to play in his first game since taking that almost miraculous pair of free throws, which he of course made despite having just suffered a complete Achilles tear. At a time like this, how could I not write about the Lakers?

As for where the idea for a *Be the General Manager* and *Choose your Own Ending Sports Adventure* book came from, such is an easy question to answer. My children and even I myself have always enjoyed *Choose Your Own Adventure* books and I have been the quintessential arm-chair General Manager for years now; simply put, I was bound to write a book like this someday. And, with the Lakers having just three players that are due any guaranteed funds at all next season, and around $29,000,000 in cap space to spend on free agents such as Carmelo Anthony, Chris Bosh, Kyle Lowry and none other than LeBron James himself, I thought now was the perfect time to write this book.

However, *Saving the Lakers* has both been a joy to write and an absolute nightmare and headache to endure. I had started writing this book before the 2013-14 season began, before Kobe Bryant signed his two-year, $48,500,000 contract, before he had subsequently re-injured himself and missed almost the entire season, before the Lakers had failed to trade Steve Nash at the trade deadline, even before the team became one of the laughing stocks of the entire NBA.

My first draft of Saving the Lakers had the opportunity to negotiate Kobe Bryant's next contract as one of the *Choose Your Own Adventure* style options built into it. My next draft factored in the Lakers making the Playoffs and therefore having the options of drafting such players as Andrew Harrison, Jahii Carson and others, rather than the top 10 talent pool they will be choosing from now. These drafts and revisions kept coming and coming and I felt like the book would never get written more than once.

Even now, as I type this introduction, I am not entirely finished with this book. At present I have them receiving the fifth pick in the draft, however depending on how the May 20th NBA Draft Lottery unfolds, things could change dramatically and an entirely new version of the book may need to be written.

This is literally the most challenging writing project I have even undertaken and that includes the sestina I wrote during my college years and the various Christian works I have authored under various pennames throughout the years. Literally, I would not wish writing this sort of book on my worst enemy. The problem is not so much that the subject matter is difficult or that the math is too advanced, but merely that the deadlines are problematic in the extreme.

Considering this book (along with *Saving the Celtics: A Be the General Manager Book*) can only be published after the *Draft Lottery* on May 20, 2013, but *before* the actual NBA Draft on June 27, 2013, which takes place a mere 31 days later, the timing of this endeavor is absolutely maddening. Basically I will need to re-write this book and create the final version within 48 hours of the *Draft Lottery* ending, get them off to my publisher for some quick editing and formatting, and then simply hope that everything is done and ready for a June 1, 2014 publication date.

That said, I had hoped to be able to publish this through one of the major publishers, receive a sizeable advance and merely reap the rewards of my work, rather than share in the risk publishing has become. However, I wasn't able to find a single major publisher who could work under such extreme deadlines. A typical publisher plans months, if not more than a year ahead, so to contact one and ask them if they could have a book published and ready to be ordered by the public a mere nine days or so after receiving the final draft is just absurd.

Regardless, I am dedicated to making this book a reality, and am sincerely praying that God's will be done. He has lead me through some of the most insane and trying experiences in the past and I trust Him to do so again with this minor dilemma this time around.

My hope is that young and old Lakers fans, stat-geeks, number-crunchers, arm-chair GM's and just plain basketball fans alike will enjoy this book and read it again and again and again, until they make all the correct choices necessary to win the championship. The truth is that winning the title on one's first read-through of this book is much, much, much harder to do than winning the NBA title is for any player in the league today, period.

There are only 30 teams in the league which means that every team starts the season with a 1-in-30 chance of winning the title or 30/1 odds. However, in order to win the championship in this book, you will have to beat incredible odds. How incredible you ask? Simply put, you literally have a better chance of actually playing in the NBA and scoring 102 points in a game than you have of winning the title on your first read-through of this book; yes, I'm serious!

The odds that you win the title on your first read through of this book are exactly 244,611,807,299 / 1. That's right two-hundred forty-four BILLION, six-hundred and eleven MILLION, eight-hundred and seven thousand, two-hundred and ninety-nine to ONE! The mathematical sum that represents such odds is $4.0881101e-12$ ... unbelievable!

Simply put, if every single one of the 7.046 billion people on the planet cloned themselves 34 times and then all 35 versions of each person on the planet tried to make it through this book and win the title on their first read-through, one person or clone on the face of the planet would actually win the title on their first attempt; one! Think about that. No seriously, really think about that; it's insane!

If you can conquer this book and win the title on your first, or even your tenth read-through, you could be a real life NBA General Manager one day. I honestly believe that, especially considering Otis Smith was once hired as a General

Manager. All of that said, read carefully, chose wisely, stay true to who you are, make the decisions you feel will help the team win the 2014-15 NBA title … and don't forget to have fun!

PREPARATION MAKES PERFECT

So you want to run the Los Angeles Lakers, eh? You want to be the General Manager of the most popular, beloved and hated professional sports franchise on the planet, eh? Then you better prepare yourself like never before!

You will only get one shot at impressing Lakers co-owner and Vice President of Basketball Operations Jim Buss. After just one meeting you will either be hired or forgotten, you will either be leading the greatest franchise in the history of the NBA or looking for work as a grade school girls basketball coach thinking about what could have been.

You've probably seen the fictional Hollywood movie *Eddie* starring Whoopi Goldberg, about a New York Knicks fan who amazingly ends up becoming coach of her favorite team. You've also probably heard the true story of the grocery bagger who became the starting QB of the St. Louis Rams and led the *Greatest Show on Turf* to a Super Bowl victory over the Tennessee Titans. The fact is that truth is literally stranger than fiction and amazing things do indeed happen every day in real life even if the majority of the masses are too jaded and desensitized to recognize such glimpses of the divine.

The fact is also that the Los Angeles Lakers just finished their worst season since moving to Los Angeles from Minneapolis in 1960! There is no better time for change than the present, especially in the championship-hungry city of angels! Jim Buss fired, err, allowed Coach Mike No-D'Antoni to resign, along with all of his assistant coaches and is about to fire General Manager Mitch Kupchak as well. The public hasn't been made aware of this latter fact and actually feels Mitch's job is safe due to the public *multi-year extension* the team gave him in April. However, the terms of that so-called *extension* were never released and the deal was little more than a parting thank you gift for the four titles Mitch had a hand in winning in the past. Kupchak will technically still be on the payroll but he is no longer truly the General Manager of this team and the public will know that soon enough. However, hopefully by that time you will be the new Lakers General Manager.

The above is Jim Buss' plan in a nut-shell; he knows full well that Laker Nation could panic when they hear the team is heading into the NBA Draft and Free Agency period without either a Coach or General Manager, therefore Mr. Buss would like to announce that Mitch Kupchak has been *reassigned within the organization* just minutes before revealing that he is thrilled to announce that a new General Manager has been chosen. Hopefully that new General Manager will be you!

You have exactly one week to prepare yourself for your interview with Jim Buss. You have just one week to have a plan in place that you can present to Mr. Buss, a plan that will not only demonstrate your remarkable understanding of the players currently under contract and those who could be signed, but of the potential draftees and how they would fit into your plans for the upcoming season, of potential coaching candidates and how they would maximize the team's performance, and of the available free agents and which ones you will be focused on signing to contracts. Most importantly, you have just one week to figure out how you will convince Jim Buss that you are the individual to lead the Los Angeles Lakers to the 2015 NBA title!

The internet is filled with a host of wonderful websites which you should familiarize yourself with as soon and as often as possible. From studying team and player salaries at HoopsHype.com, to understanding the NBA's collective Bargaining Agreement and financial aspect of completing an NBA trade at Larry Coon's CBAFAQ.com, to considering various fan-inspired trade possibilities on RealGm.com, preparation will be paramount. From getting a feel for the Lakers fans expectations at LakersNation.com, to possibly stealing a few solid ideas for how the team should proceed on draft day at BleacherReport.com, to studying the profiles of potential draft prospects at such excellent sites as draftexpress.com and nbadraft.net, you need to buckle down and prepare to read, study and think more than you have since you crammed for that high school algebra test.

You may also want to familiarize yourself with what professional sports writers, ex-players and the like feel the Lakers need to do to improve by browsing such sites as sports.yahoo.com/nba, msn.foxsports.com/nba and of course NBA.com!

You have your work cut out for you but no matter your age or credentials, if you prepare yourself for success and deliver a plan that blows Jim Buss' socks off, the job will be yours for the taking!

YOUR INTERVIEW WITH JIM BUSS

Lakers Owner Jim Buss: *Hello, my name's Jim Buss and I am the owner of the greatest professional sports team on the planet, a team you obviously want to be the General Manager of. Allow me to be blunt, I don't know you, your credentials are lacking, and frankly at this point I have no idea why I should hire you when I wouldn't even hire someone like the greatest coach of all-time in Phil Jackson or even one of the greatest players of all-time who would kill for a chance to run the Lakers such as Charles Barkley.*

However, I believe in giving people a chance and I did read the report you emailed me and was impressed; it's obvious you prepared well and have a solid plan for the future. My dad gave me a chance to put my own personal stamp on this great franchise and I'm giving you a chance to prove to me that you're the man for this job.

I have already interviewed Charles Barkley as well as a few other choice candidates including former Laker and three-time champion A.C. Green, TNT Analyst Kenny Smith, the classiest dresser in sports Craig Sager (as everyone knows

Lakers games are synonymous with fashion shows) and of course former Laker Slava Medvedenko, because, well, he's Slava Medvedenko!

However, truth be told, only A.C. Green impressed me. Kenny Smith kept ranting on and on about how his Rockets teams would have beaten the Bulls in the Finals had Jordan never retired. Barkley threatened to throw me through a window if I hired Kenny Smith over him. Slava Medvedenko actually said the job was beneath him. And Sager, well Sager disappointed me beyond belief when he showed up in a solid black suit, purple shirt and Lakers tie. I mean come on, you're interviewing for the greatest job on earth (and yes, that includes the POTUS position) and you don't have the sense to dress your best and impress your new boss with one of those fine suits you wear on television? Come on Sager you're better than that I said to myself, or at least I thought he was, but the pressure most have got to him.

All of the above said, the fact is I am going to hire A.C. Green if you don't impress me more than he did. A.C. may not have been the greatest player that has ever worn the purple and gold but he was one of the toughest, and worst case scenario with Green running the show is that we have a losing team filled with high quality individuals who will make the community proud, and frankly that's not all bad.

I'll get right to the point; if you can answer each of the following four questions correctly I will offer you a contract on the spot as Green only answered three correctly. If you can't, you can root for the Lakers from your sofa.

Question One: *If you could start next season with Kobe Bryant or LeBron James, which player would you choose?*

**If your answer to Question One is LeBron James,
turn to page 29.**

**If your answer to Question One is Kobe Bryant,
turn to page 30.**

Lakers Owner Jim Buss: *Good job, I would have thrown you out of my office had you said you'd build a team around a soon to be 36 year old Kobe Bryant over a 29 year old LeBron James. As much as I love Kobe, such an answer would have been pure idiocy.*

Continue on to page 31.

Lakers Owner Jim Buss: *Get out of my office or I'll throw you out! I love Kobe as much as anyone but only an idiot would choose to build a team around a 35 year old who is one year removed from Achilles surgery rather than a 29 year old who's won four of the past six MVP trophies and is playing better than ever.*

Youth sometimes trumps experience in basketball and genius always trumps idiocy in upper management. I hire geniuses, not idiots; goodbye.

You're journey has ended.
Enjoy being an armchair GM.

Words of Wisdom:

It's different from being 21 and you think there's endless amount of opportunities. At 33, the ending is much, much closer.

-Kobe Bryant

Lakers Owner Jim Buss: *Nice job answering the first question. However, A.C. Green also answered that question correctly. It's time for your second question.*

Question Two: *Who would you rather have shooting a wide open three pointer with the game on the line in their prime, Kobe Bryant or Steve Kerr?*

**If your answer to Question Two is Kobe Bryant,
turn to page 32.**

**If your answer to Question Two is Steve Kerr,
turn to page 33.**

Lakers Owner Jim Buss: *Have you ever considered a career as a stand-up comedian? Kobe Bryant may be one of the two best perimeter scorers in NBA history but that doesn't mean he's one of the best in every single facet of the game. If you'd really rather have a player who has never shot higher than .383 from distance over the course of a year taking the final shot instead of one of the best pure shooters the game has ever seen, a guy who averaged better than .500 on three-pointers in four different seasons and a guy who shot .454 from distance over his entire career, logic isn't your strong point.*

I simply can't trust you to build a true title-contenting roster if you can't even comprehend that players have different roles on a basketball team. It's time to go home and start rehearsing your bit funny man.

You're journey has ended.
Enjoy being an armchair GM.

Words of Wisdom:

Efficiency of performance is what wins the game for the team.

-Pat Riley

Lakers Owner Jim Buss: *Great answer! I was sure you'd get that question wrong; great answer! There aren't too many people that think rationally enough to know the best option is not always the best player. I'm impressed, however don't too excited, A.C. Green answered this question correctly as well and if there's a tie I'm going to hire the former Laker, no offense.*

Continue on to page 34.

Lakers Owner Jim Buss: *You're two for two; nice work! Of course A.C. Green answered the first two questions correctly as well so you've still got a lot of work to do. It's time for the third question.*

Question Three: *Would you ever advocate tanking (i.e. losing games on purpose) in order to improve your team's draft position?*

If your answer to Question Three is yes,
turn to page 35.

If your answer to Question Two is no,
turn to page 36.

Lakers Owner Jim Buss: *Oh baby, now you're talking! I can't believe you got that one right. Of course, I couldn't believe A.C. Green got that one right either but he did.*

Most fans see nothing wrong with a team purposely losing one or two games towards the end of the season in order to position themselves for the playoffs and give themselves the best matchup possible, yet those same fans feel it's wrong and even cheating to tank for an entire season in order to give oneself the best chance at receiving the highest draft pick possible. That's hypocritical in my book. Every Owner, General Manager and Coach is supposed to do what's best for the team, not for the league, not for the fans, but for the team and sometimes tanking is what's best, period.

Continue on to page 37.

Lakers Owner Jim Buss: *You almost made it but you blew it. I understand you may have thought I would congratulate you on saying you'd never advocate tanking, call you a high-character individual and say you're the sort of General I want leading the Lakers into battle, but you'd be mistaken.*

Whether it's losing a game at the end of the year to make sure your team gets a more favorable matchup in the first round of the playoffs, or losing a great many games to make sure your team has the best chance of landing the highest possible lottery pick it can, tanking is a necessity at times. Anyone qualified to be an NBA General Manager would know that. Get out of my office!

You're journey has ended.
Enjoy being an armchair GM.

Words of Wisdom:

Approach the game with no preset agendas and you'll probably come away surprised at your overall efforts.

- Phil Jackson

Lakers Owner Jim Buss: *Great job; you're three for three! A.C. Green was also three for three though so don't get too cocky.*

It all comes down to this final question. If you answer it correctly I will happily offer you a contract as A.C. Green did not answer this fourth question to my satisfaction. However, if you answer this question incorrectly I will hire A.C. It's as simple as that.

Question Four: *Would you ever trade or release a fan favorite or even a team legend that happens to have a bad contract or no valid role on the team going forward?*

If your answer to Question Four is yes, turn to page 38.

If your answer to Question Four is no, turn to page 39.

Lakers Owner Jim Buss: *Are you kidding me; are you kidding me right now? You did it; you actually did it!*

That was the one and only question A.C. Green answered incorrectly and I'm pretty sure I know why. You see, back on July 21, 1993 we actually released A.C. The guy had only missed three games in 8 years with us, been an All-Star and even won two NBA titles, and yet we released him. I'm sure that hurt and when I asked him the fourth question he allowed such personal hurt to cloud his judgment. He answered with emotion instead of logic and it cost him this job. However you answered every question correctly; amazing!

Congratulations, the job is yours and I'll make sure a contract is in your hands by tomorrow afternoon. Enjoy tonight, your dream is about to come true!

Continue on to page 41.

Lakers Owner Jim Buss: *I had such high hopes for you but you blew it. No individual player is above the team and any great GM knows that. A.C. Green also got this question wrong but as I said before, if this little contest of mine ends in a tie, the job would go to the former Laker and I am a man of my word. Goodbye.*

You're journey has ended.
Enjoy being an armchair GM.

Words of Wisdom:

One man can be a crucial ingredient on a team, but one man cannot make a team.

-Kareem Abdul-Jabbar

THE OFFER

Lakers Owner Jim Buss: *Today is the day, the day you get to put pen to paper and become the newest General Manager of the Los Angeles Lakers! Today is the day you get to follow in the footsteps of the great Jerry West and create your own unforgettable legacy!*

I am offering you a one year contract with a base salary of just $500,000 but with a $1,500,000 bonus due upon winning the NBA title, along with a three year option worth an additional $6,000,000 that you can opt into if we win the title this year. However, understand that there are no guarantees with this contract; if you fail to lead us to an NBA title in your very first year you will be fired.

So, what is your decision?

Decision One: Accept the contract as-is.

Decision Two: Ask for a guaranteed salary of $1,000,000 in the first year knowing that such is still below market value for such a high profile position within one of the wealthiest organizations in the league.

Decision Three: Ask for a guaranteed second year rather than a mere one year contract while making it clear that you will function better with added security which will in turn benefit the team.

If you chose Decision One, turn to page 42.

If you chose Decision Two, turn to page 43.

If you chose Decision Three, turn to page 44.

Lakers Owner Jim Buss: *Welcome to the Lakers! You have an enormous amount of work ahead of you and you better be prepared to make tough decisions and take no prisoners. The NBA Draft is right around the corner with free agency following. I'd like you to build the roster as you see fit, draft who you like, trade who you like, and sign who you want; I won't interfere and money is no object.*

Once you have the roster set the way you want it, it will be time to hire a head coach and money could be an issue as I'm not about to pay Phil Jackson type money to some middling coach like Vinny Del Negro or young up and comer from the collegiate ranks like Kevin Ollie, even if he has said that he tries to live as Christ-like as he can and has a great relationship with a superstar who I'd love to make a Laker one day in Kevin Durant, and I'm definitely not throwing mega-bucks at a collegiate legend who's never done anything of note in the NBA like John Calipari.

Now get to work and bring home that trophy!

Continue on to page 45.

Lakers Owner Jim Buss: *You greedy little punk. I offer you the keys to the kingdom and you demand more money? You disappoint me. My offer is off the table and A.C. Green will be the next General Manager of the Lakers. Get out!*

You're journey has ended.
Enjoy being an armchair GM.

Words of Wisdom:

Today's youth are told to get rich or die trying and they really shouldn't take that attitude forward with them.

- Kareem Abdul-Jabbar

Lakers Owner Jim Buss: *You blew a chance to become the General Manager of the greatest team in NBA history simply because you were greedy for a second year that may never even have come. You haven't proven anything, haven't put in one solid day's work and yet you demand a second year? Get out of my office and have fun watching A.C. Green get the dream job you could have had!*

You're journey has ended.
Enjoy being an armchair GM.

Words of Wisdom:

I believe that good things come to those who work.

- Wilt Chamberlain

DRAFT DAY

After signing your one year, win-a-ring-or-bust contract, you immediately went to work preparing for the draft, a draft that some consider to be the deepest since the 1996 NBA Draft which was perhaps the greatest draft ever. During the 96' Draft Kobe Bryant himself lasted until the 13th pick while former Laker great Derek Fisher lasted all the way to the 24th pick. Future Hall of Famers Steve Nash, Allen Iverson and Ray Allen were also selected in that legendary draft, not to mention All-Star level and standout performers such as Stephon Marbury, Antoine Walker, Jermaine O'Neal, Shareef Abdur-Rahim, Marcus Camby, Peja Stojakovic and Zydrunas Ilgauskas. There was even an undrafted rookie that year who turned out to be one of the greatest defensive players the league has ever seen by the name of Ben Wallace (the same Ben Wallace who a young Kobe Bryant absolutely posterized in summer league play but who also went on to beat the Kobe and Shaq led Lakers in the 2004 NBA Finals).

Without a second round pick in this year's draft (thanks to the horrendous July 11, 2012 trade that sent two first round and two second round picks along with cash to the Phoenix Suns for Steve Nash) you are able to focus on making just one selection, thee selection, the selection that could end up defining or destroying your entire career. After watching the Ping-Pong balls bounce and seeing your team receive the 7th pick in the 2014 NBA draft you realized the pressure was on. The Lakers are not the sort of team that finds themselves in the draft lottery very often and when they do, the fans don't expect mere professionalism, they expect perfection.

2014 will be just the third time in the past 20 years that the Lakers have had a lottery pick. The previous two selections were none other than Kobe Bryant (whom was actually drafted by the Charlotte Bobcats on behalf of the Lakers) in 1996 and Andrew Bynum in 2005. Those two players combined to win 10 Western Conference titles and 7 NBA championship rings while playing for the Lakers.

The incomparable, the great, the Logo Jerry West drafted Kobe Bryant while Mitch Kupchak drafted Andrew Bynum, yet neither are the General Manager of the Lakers today. Again, Lakers fans expect perfection; you better make this pick count!

You watched the Cleveland Cavaliers select Kansas center Joel Embiid with the number one overall pick while wondering to yourself whether he will turn out to be more Hakeem Olajuwon than Michael Olowokandi. You quietly rejoiced that you didn't have to take that risk.

Next you heard Andrew Wiggins named called and shook your head. You aren't sure if he'll be the next LeBron James or merely the next Tracy McGrady but you know for a fact you would have been happy drafting the next Tracy McGrady and would have jumped at the chance to draft Wiggins.

Duke small forward Jabari Parker was selected next by the Philadelphia 76'ers. You liked Parker's game and felt he could have been a solid young man to build around for the future; however you're not crushed that you missed out on drafting the former Blue Devil with the polished offensive game. Considering that Parker could one day disappear for a couple of years on a Mormon mission and the fact that you see more Carmelo Anthony (i.e. all offense and very little defense) in his game than you'd like to see, you smile to yourself.

When the name of the fourth pick in the draft is called you cringe. Dante Exum, the 6'6, 188 lb., 18 year old point guard from Australia is a silky smooth athlete that has the tools to play both guard positions. He also has the potential to be a strong defender as well, thanks in large part to his 6' 9.25" wingspan. He even made it abundantly clear during pre-draft interviews that he wanted to play for the Lakers and study under Kobe Bryant.

When the name of the fifth pick is called you almost let out a scream of sheer delight. Noah Vonleh, the 6'9", 247 lb. big man from Indiana was just drafted by the Utah Jazz, a shocking pick. You had thought you would most likely be drafting Noah Vonleh in a lesser of two evils type of scenario and are thrilled to see him off the board.

With the sixth pick in the draft the Boston Celtics selected Marcus Smart, the 6'4", 225 lb., 20 year old combo guard from Oklahoma State University with the rough and rugged game is now off the board. You aren't sure you would have drafted Smart with the 7th pick but he certainly would have received strong consideration, especially due to his reputation as an absolute terror on the defensive end.

However drafting Smart is no longer an option and you steel yourself to make the pick that will define you from day one in many fans minds. After what seemed like an eternity of waiting, you hear new NBA Commissioner Adam Silver declare, the Los Angeles Lakers are now on the clock.

There are three players still on the board that you have a very sincere interest in:

Shabazz Napier: This 6'1, 182 lb., soon to be 23 year old point guard is coming off his second NCAA championship and a dominant NCAA Tournament run in which he was voted the Most Outstanding Player of the Final Four. Napier is known as a gamer, for being clutch and for having the mysterious it.

Napier is a very good scorer who can get his own shot whenever he wants it and also scores efficiently as noted by his .405 three-point average and .870 free-throw average. He is also a fantastic rebounder for his size (6.7 rebounds per 40 minutes), very good passer (5.6 assists per 40 minutes) and incredibly plucky defender who seems to annoy opposing point guards each and every game he plays in.

Perhaps the only real knocks on Napier's game are that he may not have much room to improve due to his advanced age and that he does not possess elite athleticism. However, even if Napier has hit his ceiling, he is already starting point guard quality. And, while he does not have elite athleticism that does not seem to affect his on-court performances even when matched up against elite defenders like Florida's Scottie Wilbekin or much larger and stronger defenders like Kentucky's Aaron Harrison. Simply put, while Napier may be a reach this early in the draft based on his potential, or lack thereof, he may also be just about the safest pick in the draft as well and a future All-Star point guard.

Julius Randle: This 6'9", 248 lb., 19 year old power forward with the non-stop motor and bruising style of play that reminds you of a cross between Zach Randolph and Blake Griffin (or even Dominique Wilkins and Anthony Mason as strange as that sounds) won three Texas High School State Championships in four years before playing like a man among boys during his freshman season at the University of Kentucky. From his very first week on campus when he averaged 24 points while shooting over 61% from the floor and hauled in 14.3 rebounds while playing just 30 minutes per game, Randle was a monster!

Randle has all the skills a power forward needs to play at an extremely high level in the NBA. He has great footwork, can score both with his back to the basket in the post and facing up from the perimeter. He also has great explosiveness and is a nightmare for opposing defenses when running the court in transition. He's also known to be an incredibly hard worker and someone that elevates his teammates play through his sheer aggressiveness and enormous competitive spirit.

The only real knocks on Randle's game are that he is a bit turnover prone (though the same can be said for many freshman power forwards) and seems to rely on bullying his opponent to get buckets which may not be possible against bigger, stronger and better athletes at the next level. However, you're not so sure about the last point as while Randle may have a hard time scoring against the likes of Anthony Davis at the next level, there is only one Anthony Davis in the league (unless current San Francisco 49'er Anthony Davis retires from the NFL and takes his svelte 6'5", 323 lb. frame to the NBA to sign with the Milwaukee Bucks who play in his favorite state of Wisconsin) and you cannot see Randle having all that much trouble scoring against the likes of most NBA starting power forwards, including defensive dynamo's such as Jared Sullinger, Ersan Ilyasova, Josh McRoberts and Carlos Boozer, or even superstar power forwards such as Kevin Love and Dirk Nowitzki. Simply put, Julius Randle looks like exactly what a future great NBA power forward should look like at a young 19 years of age.

Doug McDermott: This 6'8, 223 lb., 22 year old combo forward and coach's son has perhaps the most complete and varied offensive game of any player in the draft if not the most dynamic and explosive. The kid known as Dougie McBuckets can score as easily in the post as he can from the perimeter and is incredibly efficient from, well, everywhere.

One major knock on McDermott is his age as he will turn 23 years old during his rookie season and therefore some seem to feel he doesn't have as much potential as other small forwards in this draft such as Croatian Dario Saric or even Syracuse sophomore wingman Jerami Grant. The other and frankly more worrisome concern with McDermott is his lack of lateral quickness and ability to guard NBA level small forwards. If you thought watching Nick Young or Ryan Kelly get burned on back door cuts and drives to the bucket was painful, imagine what someone without half of Nick Young's athleticism or even close to Ryan Kelly's length will give up on the defensive end.

Some seem to believe McDermott's ceiling could be an NBA great such as Bernard King while his floor could be a player such as Wally Szczerbiak, albeit with a better attitude and post-game. And, while Szczerbiak's name may not make one think of greatness, remember that Wally had a solid 10 year career in the league, thrice averaged over 17 points per game for an entire season, made the All-Star team and was in fact one of the best pure shooters and most efficient wing scorers in league history. That's not a bad floor all things considered.

However, will Lakers fans really be happy with you spending the 7th pick in the deepest draft since 1996 on a rich man's Wally Szczerbiak? Then again, does it matter what Lakers fans will think if such a player gives you the best opportunity to win a ring this year?

Have you decided who you will select? Are you confident in your decision? Well, before you head up to that podium to hand in your pick you might want to see who in the world would be calling you right now and pick up your ringing phone.

Toronto Raptors General Manager Masai Ujiri: *Hello, this is Masai Ujiri. Listen, I know you have to make your pick in the next couple of minutes but I wanted to propose a trade to you. By the way, this offer is not open to negotiation whatsoever, you can either take it or leave it, your call. If you agree to draft Aaron Gordon out of Arizona University for us, we will swap Chuck Hayes and Dwight Buycks who each have just one year remaining on their contracts* *for Steve Nash. We will also then draft whoever you want us to with our own first round pick later in the first round and complete this trade as soon as we are allowed to under league rules.*

I know you're probably nervous right about now and feel like the weight of the world is on your shoulders. I know you feel like you have to hit a home run with your first draft pick. I also know that my offer may not seem like a fair trade talent wise, but as I'm sure you know, a deep bench can go a long way in this league and extra cap space is worth its weight in gold this summer. Trading Nash and your pick for three players, while at the same time freeing up some extra loot to chase free agents with, may really be the perfect trade for you. That's all I have to say. That's my offer; take it or leave it.

After considering all of your draft options and hanging up the phone after speaking with Raptors General Manager Masai Ujiri you decide to:

Draft Shabazz Napier. If this is your choice,
turn to page 53.

Draft Julius Randle. If this is your choice,
turn to page 54.

Draft Doug McDermott. If this is your choice,
turn to page 55.

Trade Steve Nash and your first round pick to the Toronto Raptors for
Chuck Hayes, Dwight Buycks and their late first round pick.
If this is your choice, turn to page 56.

Lakers Owner Jim Buss: *Shabazz Napier had a solid rookie season. In fact, it wouldn't shock me if this kid becomes an All-Star before all is said and done.*

However, Shabazz just wasn't ready to play quality minutes on a championship level team as a rookie. I guess I sort of liken the struggles he had as an NBA rookie to those he had as a freshman at UCONN when he backed up Kemba Walker. He would have been a great backup point guard but he just wasn't ready to start as a rookie, let alone lead us to a title.

We might have won 49 games and snagged the fifth seed in the West but the Golden State Warriors kicked our butt in the first round and that makes me sick! You shouldn't have drafted Napier, not when you knew you had to win a title immediately. You're fired!

You're journey has ended.
Enjoy being an armchair GM.

Words of Wisdom:

I've always wanted to shoot a good percentage for my team, because I'm the point guard, and I can take fewer shots, still score more, so that I can get my teammates feeling good about themselves. That was always my feeling - that if I shoot a high percentage, I don't have to shoot a ton.

- Steve Nash

Lakers Owner Jim Buss: *It's beast time baby! Julius Randle is a beast; great pick!*

I was worried you were going to draft Doug McDermott or even Shabazz Napier. I mean, don't get me wrong, Napier could be an amazing player one day but the kid isn't ready to start at the point guard position for a title team in his first year. As for McDermott, if there's one thing that kid can do it's shoot, but he can't defend and in today's NBA you've got to be able to defend. I learned that the hard way after hiring Mike D'Antoni; wow, what a train wreck that was, just buckets after buckets after buckets with no defense to speak of.

Anyways, I am thrilled with this pick and think you just drafted a future superstar. Again, great work!

Continue on to page 57.

Lakers Owner Jim Buss: *Doug McDermott's rookie year can be summed up in one word: steady. The kid averaged16.1points per game while shooting .492 from the field and .408 from distance which is pretty awesome. In fact the kid even looks as if he could easily play a decade in this league and go down as one of the most efficient scorers in NBA history.*

However, Dougie McBuckets also had the reputation of being a bit of a black hole on the offensive end and gave up a whole lot of McBuckets on the defensive end too. Simply put, the kid couldn't guard me and you should have known that and drafted somebody else!

We might have won 45 games and earned the seventh seed in the Western Conference but we got slaughtered by the Clippers in the first round and you didn't get the job done. You're fired!

You're journey has ended.
Enjoy being an armchair GM.

Words of Wisdom:

The extra pass and the extra effort on defense always get the job done.

- Kareem Abdul-Jabbar

Lakers Owner Jim Buss: *While trading Steve Nash for an expiring contract before last season's trade deadline would most likely have saved Mitch Kupchak's GM job, trading Nash's expiring contract for two other expiring contracts, while at the same time swapping the fourth pick in the draft for a late first round draft pick, assured we wouldn't make the playoffs for the second straight season. That trade was senseless and idiotic. The Lakers and I don't do idiotic.*

I'd never hand the reins of this great franchise over to a rookie player and I should never have hired a rookie General Manager either. Feel free to apply for this position in the future as I do think you have talent, but for now, why not go gain some experience managing a D-League team? You're fired!

You're journey has ended.
Enjoy being an armchair GM.

Words of Wisdom:

As a rookie coming out of college, you don't understand the real significance of being a pro unless you're playing other pros. It doesn't help you to play sporadically here or there.

- Michael Cooper

THE DILEMA

Your team's greatest dilemma is a four letter word: Nash. Steve Nash is one of the greatest offensive point guards to ever play the game of basketball (though since defense is 50% off the game he certainly never deserved to win even one, let alone two, MVP trophies). He has also represented whatever team he played for and the entire NBA with dignity and class throughout his career. He is a first ballot Hall of Famer. However, he has also been an absolute disaster since Mitch Kupchak traded for him and has given Lakers fans yet another reason to despise the Phoenix Suns and wish Steve Nash would never have been born!

Nash is in the final year of his contract which will pay him $9,701,000. That's a whole lot of coin for a guy who seems to have a knack for finding the injury bug no matter where it's hiding.

Ordinarily you would have three options, namely, holding onto Nash and letting him finish out the final year of his contract, trading him for the best offer possible or cutting him by using the *stretch provision*, thereby paying him $3,233,667 for the next three seasons rather than the final year of his contract in full this season. However, Lakers owner Jim Buss has taken the latter option off the table. Buss was the one who brought Steve Nash to L.A. and he will not authorize you to cut him. He admitted to the fans that he made a mistake in hiring Mike D'Antoni but will not admit that trading for Nash was a mistake as the Lakers are not an organization who pays players to go play elsewhere.

All of the above said, you can either hold onto Nash and pay him his full salary or put Nash on the trade market and entertain the best offer.

If you'd like to hold onto Nash,
turn to page 59.

If you'd like to entertain the best trade offer you can get for Nash,
turn to page 60.

Lakers Owner Jim Buss: *Steve Nash suffered through yet another injury plagued season while the Lakers struggled to find any sort of cohesive identity. Does that sound familiar? It should because that is what the last two years were like before I hired you too!*

We might have won 43 games and sneaked into the playoffs but who cares when all we did was embarrass ourselves and get swept by the Thunder when we got there? I sure don't!

Albert Einstein said the definition of insanity is doing the same thing over and over again and expecting different results. You're no Einstein and I never should have hired you!

You're journey has ended.
Enjoy being an armchair GM.

Words of Wisdom:

Winning takes precedence over all. There's no gray area. No almosts.

- Kobe Bryant

The best trade offer you received for Steve Nash came from Phoenix Suns General Manager Ryan McDonough.

Phoenix Suns General Manager Ryan McDonough: *Hello, this is Ryan McDonough. I know you're looking for the best offer you can get for old man Nash. I also know that about all you've been offered to date is over-priced players on lengthy contracts.*

I'd like to make a trade happen. I believe Steve Nash deserves to play his final season in a Suns uniform and to ride off into retirement with his most adoring fans chanting his name and cheering him off the court, I really do. That said I am going to make you an offer and you can either take it or leave it. I don't have time to play games and I am making the absolute best offer I will ever make right now. I will trade you the expiring contract of Channing Frye for Steve Nash, three-million cash and unprotected second round picks in 2016 and 2017.

As you know Nash is on his last legs and Channing Frye can still contribute and be a great floor spacer with his ability to shoot the long-ball. You also know that while your owner will be sending us three-million in cash to get this deal done you will actually be gaining $2,901,000 in extra cap space and that could go a long way in signing free agents for you this summer. That's my offer; what's your answer?

If you agree to the above trade offer,
turn to page 61.

If you decline the above trade offer,
turn to page 62.

Lakers Owner Jim Buss: *Thank you. Sincerely, thank you for finding a solid trade for Nash.*

I made a major mistake in signing Nash and you just pulled a rabbit out of the hat with this trade. Channing Frye can play and I don't mind losing the three million cash if it means we have an extra $2,901,000 to spend in free agency. I also don't care about the second round picks as I expect us to be good and for those picks to be of little value anyways. Great trade!

Continue on to page 63.

Lakers Owner Jim Buss: *You refused McDonough's offer? You refused his offer! Are you kidding me?*

Having Steve Nash on the roster has been a nightmare and you refuse to trade him for a serviceable stretch four and an extra $2,901,000 in cap space? Have you lost your mind? Do you secretly work for the Suns?

I thought I hired a genius, someone who could checkmate an opposing team's General Manager and pull off great trades. I was wrong!

You're fired! You are so fired! Get out!

You're journey has ended.
Enjoy being an armchair GM.

Words of Wisdom:

These young guys are playing checkers. I'm out there playing chess.

- Kobe Bryant

RE-SIGNING YOUR OWN FREE AGENTS

After drafting Julius Randle and signing him to a contract that will see him earn a starting salary of $2,997,360 this season and trading Steve Nash to the Phoenix Suns, the only players you have under contract are Randle, Kendall Marshall (Jim Buss required you to pick up the $915,243 team option), Robert Sacre (who also will earn $915,243 this season), Channing Frye (who will earn $6,800,000) and of course, Mr. Kobe Bean Bryant (who will earn $23,500,000 this season). These five players will earn a combined $35,127,846 in the 2014-15 season.

With the salary cap set at $63,200,000 this season and the *luxury tax threshold* being set at $77,000,000 you have exactly $28,072,154 to spend on free agents. However, while having over twenty-eight million in cap space is exhilarating you must know that you have an incredible amount of work to do and a lot of hard decisions to make and the available funds may not stretch as far as you think they will.

Also, understand that under league rules you are allowed to exceed the salary cap to sign players to minimum contracts as long as you figure in a cap hold of $507,336 for each player under the 12 man limit that remains unsigned, and you do not exceed the luxury tax threshold. For example let's pretend that the Oklahoma City Thunder trio of Kevin Durant, Russell Westbrook and Serge Ibaka were all free agents this year and that each demanded and could be paid $19,544,658. A team with an empty roster could literally sign all three players to such maximum contracts as doing so would give that team a total salary of $58,633,974 and leave the team with $4,566,026 in remaining cap space as well as nine player spots to fill, and it just so happens that $4,556,026 divided nine ways works out to the NBA minimum salary of exactly $507,336, with an ole two dollar bill to spare.

The above said, if such a situation occurred and a team signed Durant, Westbrook and Ibaka, that team would not be barred from spending more than an additional $4,556,024 on the remaining nine or more players if such occurred in merely offering minimum contracts. Such a team would simply be barred from signing any one player to anything more than a *minimum contract*. However, as veterans who have played ten plus seasons in the league receive a minimum salary of $1,448,490 rather than the NBA minimum of $507,336, it is possible that the team that signed Durant, Westbrook and Ibaka to contracts totaling $58,633,974 could still sign twelve such *10-plus-season-veterans* to contracts totaling another $17,381,880. If a team were to do this, they would have an actual team salary of $76,015,854, even though the salary cap is just $63,200,000 this season, as they did not exceed the *luxury tax threshold* of $77,000,000.

All of above said, you need to be careful that you do not sign players in early free agency to standard contracts if you feel such players could be added later on minimum contracts, as to do so would be to reduce your available cap space and possibly sabotage your ability to build a title-contending roster. Simply put, you need to spend wisely or else!

The first thing you will need to do is decide which, if any, players from last year's disappointing squad you would like to re-sign, as all of them are willing to re-sign for the right price. That said it's now time to go through the list and see the contractual demands of ach player from last year's roster which you can then either accept or decline. If you accept a player's demands that player will be wearing purple and gold next season; if you decline to accept a player's demands that player will sign elsewhere.

Would you like to try and re-sign Pau Gasol immediately; knowing that if he accepts a deal you may not be able to offer max contracts to some of the upper echelon free agents? Or, would you like to simply thank Pau Gasol for his contributions to the team and inform him that you still have a sincere interest in re-signing him but that you need to focus on some of the other free agents at this time? Or, would you like to simply cut ties with Pau Gasol and make it clear to him that he is no longer a piece to the puzzle and that you will not be offering him a contract whatsoever?

If you would like to attempt to re-sign Pau Gasol immediately,
turn to page 66.

If you would like to focus on other upper echelon free agents at this
time, without closing the door on re-signing Pau,
turn to page 67.

If you would like to cut ties with Pau Gasol altogether,
turn to page 68.

Lakers Owner Jim Buss: *Do you know what money is? Do you realize that we have a limited amount of it? Focusing on re-signing Pau Gasol when you knew doing so would cost us the ability to offer other free agents maximum level contracts was a fire-able offence, a fire-able offence I refuse to forgive!*

How could you possibly think signing Pau and eliminating any chance you had at offering other free agents top dollar was a wise move? That just baffles me, completely baffles me. I thought you could remain cool under pressure but you panicked, you flat out panicked and made a horrible decision. You're fired, get out of my office and don't let the door hit you on the way out!

You're journey has ended.
Enjoy being an armchair GM.

Words of Wisdom:

    If I panic, everyone else panics.

- Kobe Bryant

Lakers Owner Jim Buss: *Great job, great job, great job, great job; oh and did I say great job? Great job!*

I can't believe you were able to convince Pau to wait patiently so you can offer big-time contracts to other free agents. However I am thrilled you were able to play Jedi mind-tricks on the Big Spaniard and convince him to be patient as maintaining our financial flexibility is paramount, especially with the likes of LeBron James and Carmelo Anthony in free agency this year. Great work!

Continue on to page 69.

Lakers Owner Jim Buss: *You cut ties with Pau Gasol? You cut ties with a man who helped return the Lakers to glory, a man who helped lead us to a three-peat in the Western Conference and back-to-back NBA titles? Do you not want the team to win basketball games? Did you wake up without a brain inside your scull? Pau Gasol is a winner and you want to dump him so you can, what, go sign some younger power forward high on potential and low on production?*

I am shocked and just absolutely dumbfounded that you could be so irresponsible, imprudent and just plain idiotic. I can't believe I hired you to run this great franchise and I can't stand to even look at you anymore. You're fired! Get out of my office and don't ever come back!

You're journey has ended.
Enjoy being an armchair GM.

Words of Wisdom:

People just don't understand how obsessed I am with winning.

- Kobe Bryant

Would you like to re-sign Nick Young to a four year $22,000,000 contract that will pay him $5,500,000 in each season and Jordan Farmar to a one year $2,750,000 contract?

If your answer is no, turn to page 70.

If your answer is yes, turn to page 71.

Lakers Owner Jim Buss: *Thank you for not re-signing Nick Young and Jordan Farmar. Young has incredible talent and can be a real game changer on the offensive end but five and a half million would have been too high a price to pay for his services. I mean, come on, he was only scheduled to make around a million before he opted out of his player option.*

As for Jordan Farmar, I actually really like his game and think he's a fine NBA point guard. However just under three-million for a third string point guard is too rich for my blood. You made a wise choice in choosing to spend your cap space elsewhere and showed great financial discipline too; nice.

Continue on to page 72.

Lakers Owner Jim Buss: *Re-signing Nick Young and Jordan Farmar wasn't a horrible decision talent wise, but signing them to contracts that paid them a total of over eight-million smackeroos was craziness. You could have spent that loot on another player or players that would have contributed much more to the team's success this season than Swaggy P and Jordy did.*

You flat out spent too much money on two role players and that prevented you from signing other quality players we desperately needed, which in turn led to a disappointing 2014-15 season. We won 47 games and earned the sixth seed and then got slapped by Dwight Howard and the Rockets.

I can't stand Dwight Coward and I can't stand losing! You're fired!

You're journey has ended.
Enjoy being an armchair GM.

Words of Wisdom:

Discipline is not a nasty word.

- Pat Riley

Would you like to re-sign Jordan Hill to a four year $24,000,000 contract with 7.5 percent annual raises that will pay him $5,393,259 this season?

If your answer is no, turn to page 73.

If your answer is yes, turn to page 74.

Lakers Owner Jim Buss: *Good decision. I really like Jordan as a player. The kid is an absolute beast on the boards and at just 27 years of age I would have loved to have kept him in purple and gold long term, just not at the price he was asking for. The kid got greedy and you didn't give in to his wild demands; nice job.*

You have to be able to make tough decisions and not blink when the stress level hits the roof and I'm thrilled you stayed cool, calm and collected and had the courage to walk away from Hill's salary demands. Had you given Jordan what he was demanding I honestly think we would have had a pretty glaring hole in our starting lineup when everything was all said and done. Great work!

Continue on to page 75.

Lakers Owner Jim Buss: *Re-signing Jordan Hill seemed like a good idea at the time but it was much more costly than you ever could have imagined. Hill's hustle, toughness and ability to snag rebounds at an alarming rate are great and all but after drafting Julius Randle you should have focused on other needs rather than a luxury like a third big man.*

Besides, Jordan is a nice player but he's not worth twenty-four million over four years; not even close! Over-spending on Hill and adding a luxury rather than a necessity served to give us an unbalanced roster this year and unbalanced rosters don't usually win rings.

We won 43 games and then got swept by the Oklahoma City Thunder. I didn't hire you to get swept; you're fired!

You're journey has ended.
Enjoy being an armchair GM.

Words of Wisdom:

I'm reflective only in the sense that I learn to move forward. I reflect with a purpose.

- Kobe Bryant

Would you like to re-sign Chris Kaman to a three year $18,000,000 contract that will pay him $6,000,000 each season and Ryan Kelly to a three year $5,100,000 contract that will pay him $1,700,000 each season?

If your answer is yes, turn to page 76.

If your answer is no, turn to page 77.

Lakers Owner Jim Buss: *Re-signing Ryan Kelly to a three year guaranteed contract worth over five-million was silly. Re-signing Chris Kaman to a three year guaranteed contract worth eighteen-million was stupid, just plain stupid!*

While Kelly is a coveted stretch four he simply isn't a trustworthy option at this point in his career. As for Kaman, I mean, he's a solid offensive center but the space cadet can't be trusted on the defensive end. Simply put, a coach can't play a player he doesn't trust.

With Kelly riding the pine and Kaman playing spot minutes we scratched our way to a seventh seed and then got handled by the Clippers. Getting handled by the should-have-been-a-Laker Chris Paul isn't what I had in mind when I hired you. You're fired!

You're journey has ended.
Enjoy being an armchair GM.

Words of Wisdom:

The hardest thing to do is to trust people.

- Dwight Howard

Lakers Owner Jim Buss: *As a baseball scout would say, you have a good eye! Don't get me wrong, Ryan Kelly has talent and a great stroke and I think he could develop into a quality player one day. However he is not a quality player at this point in his career and certainly isn't worth almost double the minimum for a second year player.*

As for Kaman, the guy baffles me. He is extremely talented, a former All-Star and plays like one of the top centers in the game. At other times it's hard to tell if he knows which sport he's playing at all.

Anyways, I'm glad you didn't overpay for either player as we need that money to spend on quality starters and not mere role players. Good job!

Continue on to page 78.

Would you like to re-sign both Wes Johnson and Xavier Henry to four year $12,000,000 contracts that will see each earn $3,000,000 this season and therefore count $6,000,000 against the salary cap

If your answer is no, turn to page 79.

If your answer is yes, turn to page 80.

Lakers Owner Jim Buss: *Good decision, I am really beginning to trust your judgment and think I hired a future 'Executive of the Year'. I would have loved to see both Wes Johnson and Xavier Henry back on the team this season as I believe they each have enormous potential, but six-million is just too much to have tied up in two role players, even if they are as young and talented as these two are.*

This was a very tough decision but you made it without blinking. I think you did a great job!

Continue on to page 81.

Lakers Owner Jim Buss: *Re-signing both Wes Johnson and Xavier Henry to contracts that paid each three-million this season turned out to be a disaster. The six-million in cap space that was tied up in the familiar Johnson and Henry could have been spent much more wisely elsewhere on an unfamiliar starter. Over-spending also prevented you from acquiring one of the top level free agents you coveted. You played it safe, were far too complacent, and it cost you.*

With Johnson being forced to start and Henry coming off the bench the team did manage to snag the sixth seed in the Western Conference after going 48-34. However they were eliminated in just five games by the Houston Rockets in the first round of the playoffs and as you know I didn't hire you to get my team knocked out in the first round; you're fired!

You're journey has ended.
Enjoy being an armchair GM.

Words of Wisdom:

When a great team loses through complacency, it will constantly search for new and more intricate explanations to explain away defeat.

- Pat Riley

Would you like to re-sign Jodie Meeks to a four year $14,000,000 contract that will pay him $3,500,000 each season?

If your answer is yes, turn to page 82.

If your answer is no, turn to page 83.

Lakers Owner Jim Buss: *Re-signing Jodie Meeks to a contract that paid him three and a half mil this season turned out to be a horrendous decision. Meeks simply wasn't a difference maker in any sense of the word and barely saw any on-court action all year.*

You simply could not afford to waste all that cap space on a specialist like Meeks, yet that's exactly what you did isn't it? With Meeks only seeing the court when long-distance shooting was an absolute must and the team having to sign a lower tier free agent due to you wasting all that loot on Jodie, we limped to a seventh place finish in the West and then got swept by the Clippers. I think this goes without saying, but I'll say it anyways, you're fired!

You're journey has ended.
Enjoy being an armchair GM.

Words of Wisdom:

You know, I have a responsibility to my team that if I'm going to be on the floor, then I have to make a difference.

- Derek Fisher

Lakers Owner Jim Buss: *Whew, I was worried. I thought you might be so intrigued by Jodie's three-point marksmanship that it would cloud your judgment and lead you to make a grave financial mistake. I'm glad you were wise with our money and decided to save the three and a half million signing Meeks would have cost us.*

However, don't you dare just sit on that money and not spend it. Go out there and woo some free agents and build a true title contender. I would rather have another ring than a few extra million in my bank account!

Continue on to page 84.

Would you like to re-sign Kent Bazemore and Marshon Brooks to two year $5,000,000 contracts that will pay each $2,500,000 per season?

If your answer is yes, turn to page 85.

If your answer is no, turn to page 86.

Lakers Owner Jim Buss: *Re-signing Kent Bazemore and Marshon Brooks to two-year five-mil contracts each was just nuts. Don't get me wrong, both kids showed promise but neither were capable starters or even dependable role players.*

The veterans on the team also felt like these young pups were more concerned with their personal stats than with the team's success. You can imagine such went over like a ton of bricks with the Black mamba.

The team, my team, limped to an eight place finish in the West and was swept by the Thunder in the first round. That said, I'm sure this won't come as a surprise; you're fired!

You're journey has ended.
Enjoy being an armchair GM.

Words of Wisdom:

A lot of young players don't really know much about the history of the game and a lot of them are missing out on what the game is all about, especially the whole concept of sportsmanship and teamwork.

- Kareem Abdul-Jabbar

Lakers Owner Jim Buss: *Once again, nice work not being suckered into signing any bad contracts. Marshon Brooks has a world of talent and Kent Bazemore is capable of being a quality role player in this league but neither is worth the money they were asking for, especially not when similar players can be picked up on minimum contracts. Your financial discipline and attention to detail is really impressive; keep up the good work!*

However, you need to understand that we only have six players under contract right now and still have a great many glaring weaknesses. You still have an enormous amount of work to do, so hit free agency running and turn this team into a contender!

Continue on to page 87

SIGNING THE LEAGUE'S FREE AGENTS

After spending exactly $35,127,846 on the five players currently under contract (Kobe Bryant, Julius Randle, Kendall Marshall, Channing Frye and Robert Sacre) and having exactly $28,072,154 left under the salary cap to spend, the pressure is on.

You, like every other basketball fan on the planet remember the dominant Chicago Bulls teams of the 90s. You remember how having a pair of All-Star perimeter players, one of whom happened to be the greatest perimeter scorer in history at that time, was a devastating combination that propelled the Bulls to six titles in 8 seasons. You have one of the two greatest perimeter scorers in history in Kobe Bryant locked up already and would love to add another All-Star level perimeter player, be it a small forward or shooting guard (as Kobe could slide over to the small forward position quite easily) alongside the Black Mamba.

There are four top-notch small forwards you are extremely interested in signing: LeBron James, Carmelo Anthony, Luol Deng and Paul Pierce. However if the price isn't right, it isn't right. Sign and spend wisely:

Would you like to sign LeBron James to a four year $85,489,136 maximum contract with 4.5 percent annual raises and a 2014-15 salary of $20,020,875?

If your answer is no, turn to page 88.

If your answer is yes, turn to page 89.

Lakers Owner Jim Buss: *You didn't offer LeBron James a contract? I must have hired a certifiable nutjob!*

LeBron James is the single most dominant player on the planet and an obvious first ballot Hall-of-Famer in the prime of his career; he is exactly the type of player the Lakers always go after. I made a mistake hiring you and would have done a better job running the team myself.

Get out of my office; you're fired!

You're journey has ended.
Enjoy being an armchair GM.

Words of Wisdom:

> *I always say, decisions I make, I live with them. There's always ways you can correct them or ways you can do them better. At the end of the day, I live with them.*
>
> *- LeBron James*

Lakers Owner Jim Buss: *Offering LeBron James a maximum contract was a no-brainer decision that even Otis Smith, Isiah Thomas and Michael Jordan couldn't have messed up. From what I'm told LeBron really appreciated the offer, was intrigued by the thought of playing with Kobe Bryant and even seriously considered playing point guard full time and reprising Magic Johnson's role as the leader of a new-era Showtime.*

However, LeBron decided to sign with his hometown Cleveland Cavaliers instead. This honestly ticks me off. I mean, come on, Dan Gilbert? Dan Gilbert? I know I might not be the great Dr. Jerry Buss but I am his kid and I've got to hold more clout than Dan Gilbert!

Whatever, it's time to move on I guess and in the words of Kevin O'Leary, LeBron James is now dead to me. Let's win a ring without the so-called king!

Continue on to page 90.

Would you like to sign Carmelo Anthony to a four year $95,923,415 maximum contract with 4.5 percent annual raises and a 2014-15 salary of $22,464,500?

If your answer is no, turn to page 91.

If your answer is yes, turn to page 92.

Lakers Owner Jim Buss: *You failed to offer Carmelo Anthony a contract? Carmelo Anthony is perhaps the best pure scorer in the NBA today and also has a good relationship with Kobe Bryant. I was looking forward to firing you!*

However, I talked with my sister Jeanie this morning and she told me she thought you made the right decision, and we both knows who wears the pants in this organization; Jeanie! Anyways, it seems she felt that Carmelo wasn't worth all the money he was asking for and that he and Kobe wouldn't be a great on-court match.

Honestly I'm not sure I agree with my sister and she has given me the power to fire you if I see fit, but I am willing to give you the benefit of the doubt for now. However, in the words of Walter Hartwell White, aka Heisenberg, since you don't really know me you might want to tread carefully, because believe you me, I am the one who knocks in this organization, at least as far as you're concerned!

Continue on to page 93.

Lakers Owner Jim Buss: *Offering a maximum contract to Carmelo Anthony would have made a great deal of sense for a team that needed a face of the franchise type star. Of course, in case you didn't realize, we already had Kobe!*

Carmelo and Kobe never quite meshed on the court and such was never clearer than on Christmas day when the game ended on a 20' fade-away jump-shot by Anthony, launched over LeBron James, despite Kobe having a mismatch in the post with Mario Chalmers guarding him. I mean come on, that's just crazy.

With Melo playing hero-ball we struggled to a sixth seed in the West and got knocked out by Dwight Coward's Rockets in the first round. You're fired!

You're journey has ended.
Enjoy being an armchair GM.

Words of Wisdom:

Of course I want to take the last shot, let's be quite frank: I've been doing for nine years already, and I've made a ton of them.

- Carmelo Anthony

Would you like to sign Luol Deng to a four year $40,000,000 contract that will pay him $10,000,000 each season?

If your answer is no, turn to page 94.

If your answer is yes, turn to page 95.

Lakers Owner Jim Buss: *You know, I actually don't know what to say about this. On one hand I think Luol Deng would have been a solid running mate for Kobe Bryant and would have helped our team tremendously, especially on the defensive side of the ball. On the other hand I feel like Deng may be breaking down and that his best ball is behind him. I also thought ten million per season was a bit much to be honest with you.*

Good job; I'm beginning to trust you more and more. Keep up the good work!

Continue on to page 96.

Lakers Owner Jim Buss: *Offering a four year $40,000,000 contract to Luol Deng was a solid decision and from what I understand Deng sincerely appreciated your offer a great deal. However while he considered what playing for the Lakers would do for his popularity and endorsement options and was extremely intrigued with playing with psycho-competitor Kobe Bryant, he just couldn't bring himself to turn down the exact same offer from the Chicago Bulls oddly enough. I mean come on, they dumped him on the Cavs last year, but, whatever floats your boat I guess, right?*

The Bulls had the money to spend after amnestying Carlos Boozer and when they realized they couldn't get Carmelo Anthony they gave their loot to Deng. It makes sense I guess.

However, don't you worry about this one bit. I'm not at all heart-broken about missing out on Deng. Just get back on the horse and build me a title winning roster!

Continue on to page 96.

Would you like to sign Paul Pierce to a two year $20,000,000 deal that will pay him $10,000,000 each season?

If your answer is no, turn to page 97.

If your answer is yes, turn to page 98.

Lakers Owner Jim Buss: *Eh, what I can say, I'm not that disappointed you didn't sign Paul Pierce. I never liked that ex-Celtic anyways and besides he's older than Methuselah!*

Good job holding onto our cap space. Let the Nets overpay for old man Pierce or the Clippers sign him to a Doc-Rivers discount. I don't care; I don't want him on my team! Great work!

Continue on to page 99.

Lakers Owner Jim Buss: *Signing Paul Pierce to a two year $20,000,000 contract was a bad decision. Pierce only played 45 games for us this year and struggled to mesh with Kobe Bryant, often times seeming to feel he should be the team's number one option, which is just stupid!*

I was pleasantly surprised to see us finish the season with 50 wins and nab the fifth seed in the Western Conference. However the Warriors killed us in the first round with Andre Iguodala shutting Pierce down game in and game out, holding him to just 11.5 points per game.

The Warriors knocked us out in six games and I didn't hire you to win two measly playoff games; I hired you to win a ring. You're fired!

You're journey has ended.
Enjoy being an armchair GM.

Words of Wisdom:

At the beginning of the season, I set my goal to see if I can lead the league in scoring, because I feel I have that kind of ability. A lot of guys say it, but it's not really in their grasp. I feel that's really in my grasp.

- Paul Pierce

Pau Gasol's agent Arn Tellem has just informed you that Pau will be accepting a three year $27,000,000 contract with a third year team option from the Dallas Mavericks and signing on the dotted line in the next five minutes unless you agree to match this offer and re-sign him.

Would you like to sign Pau Gasol to a three year, $27,000,000 contract with a third year team option, 7.5 percent annual raises and a starting salary for this season of $8,372,094? Or, would you rather move on and allow Pau to sign with the Mavericks?

If you would like to decline Pau's offer and allow him to sign with the Dallas Mavericks,
turn to page 100.

If you would like to sign Pau Gasol to a three year $27,000,000 deal,
turn to page 101.

Lakers Owner Jim Buss: *Failing to re-sign Pau Gasol was a bonehead move. Gasol wasn't merely a two-time champion and possibly one of the most skilled low-post players in the history of the league, he was a great locker-room presence, wonderful teammate and trusted running mate of Kobe Bryant.*

I understand Pau isn't getting any younger and his defense has declined, however even last year playing for the mess that was Mike D'Antoni, he still managed to average around 21 points, 13 rebounds, 4 assists and 2 blocks per 40 minutes. In fact, over a 10 game span last January the guy averaged 21.8 points and 11.9 rebounds while shooting .530 from the field. Those are superstar numbers!

I'm disgusted with the lack of respect you had for Pau as a person and even more so as a basketball player. Get out, you're fired!

You're journey has ended.
Enjoy being an armchair GM.

Words of Wisdom:

It doesn't matter who gets what. It's just a matter of doing what it takes to win.

- Pau Gasol

Lakers Owner Jim Buss: *Great job signing Pau Gasol. The big Spaniard is an integral part of our success going forward and I've often been shocked and disappointed in the way Pau has been treated by the fans after all he's done for this team.*

The guy has won three conference titles, two rings and been the epitome of a great teammate. You can't really ask for anything more if you're an owner and I'm thrilled you saw Pau's true value as both a player and teammate. With Pau on board I expect great things this season; great work!

Continue on to page 102.

After signing Pau Gasol to a three year $27,000,000 contract with a starting salary for this season of $8,372,094 you have spent exactly $43,499,940 on the six players currently under contract (Kobe Bryant, Pau Gasol, Julius Randle, Kendall Marshall, Channing Frye and Robert Sacre) and have exactly $19,700,060 left under the salary cap to spend.

Jim Buss believes the team has its starting shooting guard, power forward and center already on the roster in Kobe Bryant, Julius Randle and Pau Gasol. However you still do not have a starting small forward and need one desperately and the only two starting level small forwards who are interested in signing with the Lakers are Danny Granger and Trevor Ariza.

Would you like to sign Danny Granger to a two year $16,000,000 deal that will pay him $8,000,000 each season? Or, would you like to sign Trevor Ariza to a four year $28,000,000 deal with 4.5 percent annual raises and a starting salary next season of $6,557,377.

If you would like to sign Granger, turn to page 103.

If you would like to sign Ariza, turn to page 104.

Lakers Owner Jim Buss: *Granger ended up playing in just 20 games for us this season; twenty games! And, what really burns me is that this wasn't some out of the blue occurrence; you should have seen this coming!*

With Granger catching every injury bug in the building we limped to a 42-40 record and an eighth seed in the Western Conference. To make matters worse I had to watch my team get destroyed in four straight games by the Thunder while the guy I was paying $8,000,000 to sat on the bench in street clothes nursing a silly toe injury.

You're fired, fired, fired, fired!

You're journey has ended.
Enjoy being an armchair GM.

Words of Wisdom:

I've played with IVs before, during and after games. I've played with a broken hand, a sprained ankle, a torn shoulder, a fractured tooth, a severed lip, and a knee the size of a softball. I don't miss 15 games because of a toe injury that everybody knows wasn't that serious in the first place.

- Kobe Bryant

Lakers Owner Jim Buss: *You signed Trevor? You signed Trevor! Now that's what I'm talking about; great signing!*

I love Trevor Ariza's game, just love it. We would never have won the 2009 NBA title without Trevor. He was amazing on the defensive end of the floor and turned into a real shot-maker on the offensive end of the floor that year as well. To this day I wish we could have kept Trevor in purple and gold and just added Metta World Peace to our roster, rather than having to let Trevor walk in order to bring Metta in; had we done that we would have at least one more ring than we do in my opinion.

I'm thrilled with this signing and feel Trevor will play the best ball of his entire career over the next four years, so to have him locked up for the long-term is just fantastic. The guy is only 29 years old and is coming off a year in which he helped lead the once laughable Washington Wizards to the playoffs while averaging around 16 points, 7 rebounds, 3 assists and 2 steals and shooting a career high in 3-point percentage. Trevor is an all-out baller; great signing!

Continue on to page 105.

After signing Trevor Ariza you have spent exactly $50,057,317 on the seven players currently under contract (Kobe Bryant, Pau Gasol, Julius Randle, Trevor Ariza, Kendall Marshall, Channing Frye and Robert Sacre) and have exactly $13,142,683 left under the salary cap to spend.

Jim Buss believes the team now has four starters on the roster in Kobe Bryant, Julius Randle, Pau Gasol and Trevor Ariza and that at least one more starter-level free agent must be added, if not two (with the second serving as the team's sixth man). At this point Jim Buss wants to see you sign the best single player available or the best free agent duo available, depending on salary and how you see each player fitting in with the team.

The above said, Jim Buss has authorized you to give one free agent a starting salary of up to $11,113,339 and to sign four free agents to minimum contracts, or to give two free agents a combined starting salary of up to $11,620,675 and to sign three free agents to minimum contracts.

The choice is yours. Spend wisely.

Before pursuing other options there are two pairs of teammates that are prepared to sign contracts with their former teams but which would like to give you the opportunity to sign them first.

Michael Beasley and Greg Oden who both played last season for the Miami Heat are each interested in signing four year $20,000,000 contracts with 4.5 percent annual raises and starting salaries of $4,638,841 which would add a total of $9,277,682 to this season's payroll.

Patrick Patterson and John Salmons who both played last season for the Toronto Raptors are each interested in signing one year $4,750,000 contracts which would add a total of $9,500,000 to this season's payroll.

**If you would like to sign Michael Beasley and Greg Oden,
turn to page 107.**

**If you would like to sign Patrick Patterson and John Salmons,
turn to page 108.**

**If you do not want to sign either duo,
turn to page 109.**

Lakers Owner Jim Buss: *Signing Michael Beasley and Greg Oden was a risky decision. Both players have shown flashes of superstardom while at the same time showing flashes of absolute incompetence and immaturity. I gave you a title or bust ultimatum and taking such an enormous risk was extremely unwise.*

With Michael Beasley doing what Michael Beasley does, namely shoot, score, shoot, play average defense and shoot some more and Greg Oden doing what Greg Oden does, namely, get injured, rebound, get injured, block shots and get injured some more, my Lakers were a maddeningly inconsistent team. When everything was said and done we backed into the playoffs with a 49-33 record after earning the fifth seed in the West. Then, we got our heads handed to us by the Golden State Warriors with Greg Oden missing the entire series with a back injury.

The risk you took back-fired. Now, you're fired!

You're journey has ended.
Enjoy being an armchair GM.

Words of Wisdom:

You can't win if you don't play as a unit.

- Kareem Abdul-Jabbar

Lakers Owner Jim Buss: *Signing the duo of Patrick Patterson and John Salmons was a mistake. Salmons was a huge disappointment and simply didn't see enough on-court action to justify his salary. And, when he was on the bench he seemed to have no interest in the game or in rooting for his teammates. Patrick Patterson on the other hand showed promise and looks like he could turn out to be a fine role player who could play a decade plus in this league. However, having Patterson on the roster served to actually stunt the rapid growth of Julius Randle and when Randle started playing major minutes in the final quarter of the season Patterson seemed to pout over his lack of playing time.*

Needless to say, you blew it. You're fired!

You're journey has ended.
Enjoy being an armchair GM.

Words of Wisdom:

I'll do whatever it takes to win games, whether it's sitting on a bench waving a towel, handing a cup of water to a teammate, or hitting the game-winning shot.

- Kobe Bryant

Lakers Owner Jim Buss: *You're lucky, you know that? You have no idea how fast I would have fired you if you had signed either Michael Beasley and Greg Oden or Patrick Patterson and John Salmons.*

I wasn't worried though. You have shown real basketball intelligence from the beginning and I had no doubt you would pass on signing these two tandems when I heard about their desire to play for the Lakers. You have to understand that just about every free agent on the planet wants to play in Los Angeles and not for the Paper-Clips either.

Chris Paul's arrival has obviously made the Paper-Clips a much, much more attractive free agent destination, but let's not forget that Chris Paul was supposed to be a Laker and would have been a Laker if not for Fuhrer Stern's bizarre nixing of our trade for the little magician, due to so-called 'basketball reasons'. Well, the Lakers are basketball, period!

Anyways, great job not signing either of these tandems to contracts and saving our cap space for more attractive options.

Continue on to page 110.

Before pursuing further options on the free agent market, the agents for both Lance Stephenson and Evan Turner have contacted you, stating that they believe if you offer either young star a four year $38,000,000 contract with a starting salary of $8,899,298 and 4.5 percent annual raises, the Indiana Pacers will refuse to match such an offer and one of these top young stars will be yours.

If you would like to offer Evan Turner a four year $38,000,000 contract, turn to page 111.

If you would like to offer Lance Stephenson a four year $38,000,000 contract, turn to page 112.

Lakers Owner Jim Buss: *I have two words for you, stats lie! Simply put, Evan Turner was what Kenny Smith likes to call a 'looter in a riot' last season, racking up great stats on a horrible Philadelphia 76'ers team. Lance Stephenson on the other hand may have had more modest statistics but he was also playing for one of the best teams in the league and contributing in various ways that don't show up on mere stat sheets. And, when Turner got to Indy late last season, Lance was still the man Coach Frank Vogel turned to in crunch time.*

I would have let you slide in signing Turner over Stephenson if you were also able to save some cap space to sign another decent free agent along with Turner. However, you not only offered a contract to the wrong player, you offered way, way, way too much m-o-n-e-y as well.

It literally pains me to say this as you've shown great promise; however, you're fired!

You're journey has ended.
Enjoy being an armchair GM.

Words of Wisdom:

I'm tired of hearing about money, money, money, money, money.

- Shaquille O'Neal

Lakers Owner Jim Buss: *Offering Lance Stephenson a four year $38,000,000 contract was a solid decision. I believe Lance would have made a great running mate for Kobe and Pau as well as a true building block for the future. However, Larry Bird obviously felt the same way about Lance as I did, because the Pacers matched your offer.*

Regardless, you've done an amazing job so far and I am thrilled with your decision making. Keep up the good work!

Oh, by the way, Evan Turner is no longer an option either as he just signed a contract with some middling team where he can rack up more empty statistics. Personally I think you dodged a bullet with Evan as while he's a fine young player I don't think he's worth the money he was asking for.

Why don't you watch Rise of the Planet of the Apes to de-stress (and as a primer to Dawn of the Planet of the Apes which is coming out soon) and then come out ready to dominate like Caesar!

Continue on to page 113.

You just learned that the Dallas Mavericks have offered Dirk Nowitzki a two year contract and that the German gunslinger is about to put pen to paper and accept their offer. However, there is an outside chance that if you offer Nowitzki every penny you have left under the cap and a guaranteed three year contract with a third year player option as well, he will take such an offer to heart, be flattered at your sincerity and obvious appreciation for his game and sign with the Lakers.

Would you like to offer Dirk Nowitzki to a three year $34,840,318 deal with 4.5 percent annual raises and a starting salary of $11,113,339 with the final season being a player option?

If your answer is no, turn to page 114.

If your answer is yes, turn to page 115.

Lakers Owner Jim Buss: *You didn't offer Dirk Nowitzki a contract? I don't care how good you've done so far, that is an inexcusable gaffe. I realize that had you offered such a contract and had Dirk accepted you would have no more room under the cap to sign anything but minimum contract players but I don't care; we're talking about Dirk Nowitzki, the greatest European NBA player ever!*

Dirk Nowitzki would have assured this team a title in my eyes. The guy just does everything right. He may not be an athletic freak but he knows how to win and is the ultimate professional. Plus we would have kicked Mark Cuban where it hurts which can only be a good thing in my mind.

You should have done whatever it took to get Dirk on the team. You failed and now you're fired!

You're journey has ended.
Enjoy being an armchair GM.

Words of Wisdom:

I try to do the right thing at the right time. They may just be little things, but usually they make the difference between winning and losing.

- Kareem Abdul-Jabbar

Lakers Owner Jim Buss: *Offering Dirk Nowitzki all the funds you had left under the salary cap was an absolute no-brainer decision. In fact, I would have fired you on the spot had you failed to offer the greatest European player in NBA history a contract.*

However, while Dirk strongly considered the offer and thought finishing out his career here in Los Angeles with Kobe Bryant and Pau Gasol would have been amazing, he simply couldn't pass up the opportunity to retire with the only team he has ever suited up for in the Dallas Mavericks.

Of course, knowing Mark Cuban like I do, I wouldn't be surprised if he told Dirk that his jersey would never hang from the rafters of the American Airlines Center if he signed with us. Remind me to slap Cuban the next time I see him.

Regardless, you did your job and did it well. I can't ask for anything more. Keep up the good work.

Continue on to page 116.

Before pursuing further options on the free agent market, the agents for both Marcin Gortat and Kyle Lowry have contacted you. Gortat's agent stated that if you offer his client a four year $36,000,000 contract with $9,000,000 due each season, his client will sign on the dotted line. Lowry's agent stated that if you offer his client a four year $40,000,000 contract with $10,000,000 due each season, his client will happily sign with the Lakers.

If you would like to sign Marcin Gortat to a four year $36,000,000 contract,
turn to page 117.

If you would like to sign Kyle Lowry to a four year $40,000,000 contract,
turn to page 118.

Lakers Owner Jim Buss: *Marcin Gortat? You signed Marcin Gortat over one of the best point guards on the planet, a guy who helped change the entire culture of the Toronto Raptors franchise and led them to the playoffs last season? Why?*

I mean, don't get me wrong, Marcin is my favorite Marcin, though I have always been a fan of Marvin, even though he planned to blow up this great planet because it obstructed his view of Venus. However, signing Gortat over Lowry was just obscene. I actually feel like I'm in a cartoon with Marvin the Martian right now and that it was you Marvin was talking about when he said, 'Oh no, he's turned into a Neanderthal rabbit.'

You're fired. Now brace yourself for immediate disintegration!

You're journey has ended.
Enjoy being an armchair GM.

Words of Wisdom:

You have no choices about how you lose, but you do have a choice about how you come back and prepare to win again.

- Pat Riley

Lakers Owner Jim Buss: *In my mind Kyle Lowry is the perfect choice to run the point for the Lakers, the perfect choice! Lowry is a little bulldog with a huge heart and a warrior's mentality. Offering a contract to Kyle, even a fourt-million dollar one, over my favorite Marcin was a wise decision.*

Of course, I believe in destiny and I guess it wasn't Kyle Lowry's destiny to run the point for the greatest professional sports team on the planet as I just heard from his agent that he decided to accept an offer from the Toronto Raptors. However, you proved your chops once again by making the right offer to the right player and I couldn't ask for anything more.

By the way, Marcin Gortat has decided to re-sign with the Washington Wizards as well, so he's off the market too. Not to worry though, I actually didn't think Gortat was worth the price he was asking.

You did your job and did it well. Keep up the good work but also understand that we still need another potential star or solid free agent duo to really have a shot at contending for the title this season. You've done great so far but you still have some big decisions to make!

Continue on to page 119.

After focusing on various star players and having had to wait and wait and wait while the Indiana Pacers decided what to do with Lance Stephenson, urgency has set in. Jim Buss has demanded you sign either a potential star player or solid free agent duo immediately so that you can turn your full attention to hiring a coach before all of the top coaching candidates are snapped up as well.

The above said there are four intriguing options left for you on the free agency market.

The first is signing the duo of Jerryd Bayless and Kris Humphries. Bayless and Humphries played together in Boston last season and each will agree to a four year $20,000,000 contract with a starting salary of $4,683,841 and 4.5 percent annual raises. Both Bayless and Humphries were former lottery picks that never quite lived up to their potential but could blossom into fine players with the Lakers.

The second option is signing the duo of Jimmer Fredette and Andray Blatche who are also each offering to sign on the dotted line if they are offered four year $20,000,000 contracts with starting salaries of $4,683,841 and 4.5 percent annual raises. Fredette was the 10th pick in the draft just three short years ago and while he has never come close to producing in the NBA like he did as the star of Brigham Young University in college he can still shoot the ball better than 95% of NBA players and his per-40 stats have always been solid; perhaps he just needs an opportunity to play major minutes?

Andray Blatche on the other hand was a mega-contract player just a few shorts years ago in Washington where his immaturity led to his being amnestied by the Wizards. Since then Blatche has matured, improved and become a per-40 star in Brooklyn while averaging over 21 points, 10 rebounds, and 3 combined steals and blocks per 40 minutes for the Nets; he also may need nothing more than some solid minutes to turn into something special in this league.

The third option is signing the 28 year old former Detroit Piston Rodney Stuckey, a combo guard who just seems to be entering the prime of his career and may turn into a quality starter in Los Angeles or even the top 6th man in the entire league. Stuckey, also known as *Chief Lightning First Step* blew up in his third season in the league (2009-10) when he averaged 16.6 points, 4.8 assists, 3.8 rebounds and 1.4 steals per game. After a rough 2012-13 season Stuckey bounced back last year and transformed himself into one of the top 6th men in the league while averaging over 20 points per 40 minutes.

Rodney Stuckey has made it clear through his agent that he is willing to accept a slight decrease in pay from the $8,500,000 he earned last season to play for the Lakers. He will sign on the dotted line if he is offered a four year $32,000,000 contract with a starting salary of $7,494,146 and 4.5 percent annual raises. This said, signing Stuckey would leave you with the ability to sign one more free agent to a contract starting at $2,098,791 if you so desired.

The fourth and final option available to you is offering a contract to the 9th pick in the 2010 draft, Gordon Hayward. Hayward is coming off a breakout season in which he averaged career highs in points, rebounds, assists and steals all while being the focal point of opposing defenses game in and game out.

While Hayward is a restricted free agent it is common knowledge that the Utah Jazz are prepared to offer him no more than right around $38 – 40 million over 4 years. It's also common knowledge that the Boston Celtics and former Butler University coach Brad Stevens are also extremely interested in signing Hayward, though unless they can quickly find a trade partner to absorb the salary of Gerald Wallace, Brandon Bass or Jeff Green the Celtics won't be able to make him a truly competitive offer.

The above said, if you immediately throw your entire remaining cap space at Hayward in the form of a four year $47,453,958 contract with a salary of

$11,113,339 due each season, the Celtics would instantly be out of the running and the Jazz may not match such an offer, choosing instead to use their cap space to sign other free agents while building around a Trey Burke and Alec Burks backcourt.

**If you would like to sign Bayless and Humphries,
turn to page 122.**

**If you would like to sign Fredette and Blatche,
turn to page 123.**

**If you would like to sign Stuckey,
turn to page 124.**

**If you would like to sign Hayward,
turn to page 125.**

**If you do not want to sign any of the above and instead desire
to keep your cap space intact,
turn to page 126.**

Lakers Owner Jim Buss: *Two Boston Celtics? You just had to sign two of those leprechauns? In all seriousness, I was disgusted with this signing when it happened, knew we would not win a title and history proved me right. Bayless and Humphries weren't bad players for us this year, they just weren't the players we needed on our roster to win a title. Both of them seemed more interested in their own stats than in actually winning ballgames and that just won't work here in Los Angeles.*

I understand we had a solid season winning 50 games and earning the seventh seed in the Western Conference. However the Clippers knocked us out in the first round; they made is look like a junior high squad and that makes me sick!

I could have hired Tracy McGrady as coach if all I wanted to do was to get into, but not out of, the first round of the Playoffs.

Why don't you buy a copy of 'Bryant T. Jordan's 'Saving the Celtics' and try to beat that book, because, you're fired!

You're journey has ended.
Enjoy being an armchair GM.

Words of Wisdom:

Ask not what your teammates can do for you. Ask what you can do for your teammates.

- Magic Johnson

Lakers Owner Jim Buss: *I have to admit that I was excited when you signed Jimmer Fredette and Andray Blatche as I really thought they would be great additions. However, I'm not the GM of this team, you are and you should have known better!*

Jimmer and Andray always showed flashes of excellence but once they got those four year guaranteed contracts you handed them it was as if they had no reason to improve any longer. It's like they lost their hunger and that really upsets me because you should have seen that coming!

Fredette and Blatche would make a great duo in some 2-on-2 streetball tournament but they did little more than put up empty stats for us this season. We earned a fifth seed in the West after winning 50 games, sure, but we also got lit up by the Warriors and knocked out in 5 games. You're fired!

You're journey has ended.
Enjoy being an armchair GM.

Words of Wisdom:

I'm hungrier than those other guys out there.

- Dennis Rodman

Lakers Owner Jim Buss: *Rodney Stuckey? You tied your fortunes as the Lakers GM to Rodney Stuckey? After watching the team struggle to earn a mere fifth seed in the Western Conference and then lose a tough six game series to the Golden State Warriors, do you think you made the right choice?*

Obviously that was a rhetorical question as I really don't care to hear what you have to say. Stuckey wasn't bad as a combo guard but when we needed him to run the point effectively, he just couldn't get the job done. One game he would play like his nickname 'Chief Lightning First Step' and the next he would play like the ghost of a one-legged Drazen Petrovic.

Talent is great but consistency is better. Potential is great but production is better. You have talent and potential but didn't get the job done. You're fired!

You're journey has ended.
Enjoy being an armchair GM.

Words of Wisdom:

The NBA has the best point guards in the world, so it is important that I come ready to play every night.

- Steve Nash

Lakers Owner Jim Buss: *Richie Rich is in the house and I'm feeling good! I don't know why Gordon Hayward reminds me of Richie Rich but he does; I always liked Richie and I like Gordon even more. I'm thrilled with this signing!*

Believe it or not I was the one non-Mormon outside of the state of Utah that actually watched Jazz games last year. I'm serious. I watched Jazz games simply to see Gordon Hayward play and I loved what I saw. The kid has really worked on his game a great deal and reminds me of a young James Harden. He may never turn into an MVP candidate like Harden has in Houston but the kid is extremely skilled and can do it all on a basketball court.

Honesty I almost called you to demand you offer Hayward all the cap space we had but I decided against it after my sister told me to just chill out and trust you. As usual Jeanie was right and as usual you have proved to be the right man for the job. Great work!

Continue on to page 127.

Lakers Owner Jim Buss: *I still can't believe you didn't sign anyone with the remaining nine-million plus in cap space you had to play with? What in the world were you planning to do with the extra cap space, pocket it and escape to Costa Rica like 'Ivan Block' in 'Runner Runner'?*

I told you that you would have to win a title this year or that you'd be fired. Then you go out and refuse to spend the cap space we had? Did you think you were playing Moneyball with Billy Bean? Crazy! I don't even know what to say at this point. It's as if you had no interest at all in actually winning a ring.

We now have no options left and I have lost all faith in you. I cannot in good conscience allow you to hire our next coach or even keep your job. You're fired, effective immediately; now get out!

You're journey has ended.
Enjoy being an armchair GM.

Words of Wisdom:

There's always the motivation of wanting to win. Everybody has that. But a champion needs, in his attitude, a motivation above and beyond winning.

- Pat Riley

Your current roster looks as follows:

Starting Point Guard:	Kendall Marshall	$915,243
Starting Shooting Guard:	Kobe Bryant	$23,500,000
Starting Small Forward:	Trevor Ariza	$6,557,377
Starting Power Forward:	Julius Randle	$2,997,360
Starting Center:	Pau Gasol	$8,372,094
Backup Point Guard:		
Backup Shooting Guard:	Gordon Hayward	$11,113,339
Backup Small Forward:		
Backup Power Forward:	Channing Frye	$6,800,000
Backup Center:		
Reserve Point Guard:		
Reserve Shooting Guard:		
Reserve Small Forward:		
Reserve Power Forward:		
Reserve Center:	Robert Sacre	$915,243
Total Team Salary:		$61,170,656

You now have exactly $61,170,656 invested in the eight players on your roster and have only $2,029,344 left in cap space which means you will only be able to sign players to minimum contracts from here on out. Jim Buss has ordered you to sign one backup point guard and one backup small forward as well as five reserve players to equip the team with the maximum allowable 15 players under contract.

The first order of business is signing a backup point guard and small forward. There are three realistic minimum contract duos available. Choose wisely.

The first option is signing the duo of Beno Udrih and Richard Jefferson. Udrih has been a quality back-up point guard for the past three seasons after playing starter minutes the previous four seasons in Sacramento. During his time with the Knicks last season Udrih gave them steady minutes at the point evidenced by his 7.5 assists per 40 minutes and 2.6 assists to turnover ratio. Richard Jefferson is also a dependable veteran small forward who had a sort of bounce-back season last year playing for the Jazz after enduring a very rough 2012-13 season with Golden State.

The second option is signing the duo of Devin Harris and Antawn Jamison. Harris may not be the player he was at 25 years of age when he averaged 21.3 points and 6.9 assists as the Nets starting point guard but he still puts up quality numbers and is a dependable option for a playoff level squad just as he was with the Dallas Mavericks last season. Antawn Jamison's best days are well behind him, however he is still a quality teammate, great locker-room guy and a veteran voice the younger players can learn from; he could well be worth a minimum contract.

The third option is signing a duo of former Lakers: Jordan Farmar and Metta World Peace. While the Lakers used the amnesty provision on Metta World Peace last season in order to save money, it is common knowledge that Lakers management and especially superstar Kobe Bryant adore the mercurial small forward with the lightning fast hands and samurai mentality. World Peace may not be the elite defender he once was but he is still a capable defender who brings an enormous amount of toughness to whatever team he plays for. As for Jordan Farmar, he played fantastic basketball for the Lakers just last season. While his stats may have been inflated due to the team's meager roster and torrid offensive pace the fact remains that Farmar has improved his overall game and especially his three-point marksmanship a great deal since helping the Lakers to back-to-back titles in 2009-10 and could be a magnificent minimum contract signing.

If you would like to sign Udrih and Jefferson,
turn to page 130.

If you would like to sign Harris and Jamison,
turn to page 131.

If you would like to sign Farmar and World Peace,
turn to page 132.

Lakers Owner Jim Buss: *When you signed Beno Udrih and Richard Jefferson over Jordan Farmar and Ron Artest I threw my Artest autographed basketball so hard at my office wall that it rebounded, hit me in the face and gave me a black eye. When I actually watched Beno Udrih and Richard Jefferson play uninspired basketball I wanted to hire Artest to give you a black eye!*

With Udrih and Jefferson serving as the team's backup point guard and small forward we won a whopping 43 games and earned a disappointing eighth seed in the Western Conference. The team you assembled then went out and got embarrassed by the Oklahoma City Thunder losing four straight games by a total of 83 points; 83 points!

If I wanted to watch uninspired ball and get swept in the first round I would have kept D'Antoni. You're fired!

You're journey has ended.
njoy being an armchair GM.

Words of Wisdom:

I am not a passenger in anything I do.

- Derek Fisher

Lakers Owner Jim Buss: *Signing Devin Harris and Antawn Jamison over Jordan Farmar and Ron Metta World Peace Artest was an abomination. Did you even watch Antawn Jamison play last year? The guy averaged 3.8 points per game with the Clippers; 3.8 points! He shot under .200 from deep and stunk it up from the field as well. I mean come on; the guy will be celebrating his 39th birthday by the time the Finals start which might as well be his 390th birthday. The guy is finished!*

My team, not your team, my team wasn't good enough to win a title this season because the roster you put together wasn't good enough, period. We may have sneaked into the playoffs as an eighth seed but when we got there we got slapped around by the Thunder 4-0. That makes me sick!

You failed. I didn't hire you to fail. You're fired!

You're journey has ended.
Enjoy being an armchair GM.

Words of Wisdom:

Look for your choices, pick the best one, then go with it.

- Pat Riley

Lakers Owner Jim Buss: *Ron Artest, I don't like calling him Metta World Peace because he didn't win a title as Metta World Peace, and Jordan Farmar were great signings! I'm thrilled you signed these two former ring-winning Lakers rather than the other nonsense options that were available to you. Nice work!*

Jordan is really undervalued in my view and could easily step in and play starter's minutes at the point if Kendall Marshall gets injured or loses his outside stroke. Ron might be a little bit of a headache but I just love the guy. We won our last title with him and the poor guy ended up giving his ring away to charity. I'd love to see him win another ring so he can actually wear it on his finger and show the world he's a champion.

Anyways, I 'm ecstatic with how the roster is shaping up and can't wait to see this team in action. You still need to fill out the roster of course, and most importantly you need to hire a coach that can lead the roster you build to a title; so, you still have a lot of work to do but great work so far!

Continue on to page 133.

The next order of business is signing a backup center as Jim Buss does not feel that Robert Sacre can be trusted to play starter's minutes at this stage of his career if Pau Gasol happens to miss extended time for any reason. There are three players who are willing to accept a minimum contract that are also suitable options. Choose wisely.

Matt Bonner is a 34 year old power forward / center who has played for the San Antonio Spurs for the past 8 seasons. His playing time has been on the decline as has his production. However, Bonner is still a deadly three point shooter who can stretch the defense as well as any other big in the game today.

Emeka Okafor is a former #2 pick and NBA Rookie of the Year who has thrice finished in the top 10 in total rebounds and blocks. During the 2012-13 season Okafor averaged just under 10 points and 9 rebounds per game while also averaging a robust 14.9 points, 13.5 rebounds and 1.5 blocks per 40 minutes. However, he failed to play in even one game last season as he was injured. Simply put, Emeka could be a stud and an absolute steal or he could be an injury plagued bust.

B.J. Mullens was the 24th pick in the 2009 NBA Draft and two seasons ago he averaged over 10 points and 6 rebounds per game while showing the ability to stretch out defenses and hit the 3-ball while playing for the Charlotte Bobcats. However, last season he struggled to get any meaningful playing time at all while with the Clippers and averaged just 2.5 points and 1.2 rebounds per game with a playoff level team. Mullens is still just 25 years old however and his best basketball could be ahead of him.

**If you would like to sign Matt Bonner,
turn to page 135.**

**If you would like to Emeka Okafor,
turn to page 136.**

**If you would like to sign B.J. Mullens,
turn to page 137.**

Lakers Owner Jim Buss: *I don't know what gave you the idea that signing Matt Bonner would be a good idea. I'm guessing you just thought it would be cool to have the Red Mamba and Black Mamba on the same team. Honestly, I would have even rather had you sign a former Celtic than a former Spur, if for no other reason than that Spurs players are the epitome of system players. Just as D'Antoni's system made Steve Nash an MVP, Gregg Popovich's system turns otherwise average players into quality role players and goofy GMs like you later overpay to sign them.*

With Bonner playing as if he wished he was still in San Antonio we still managed to win 50 games and nab the fifth seed in the Western Conference. We even gave the Golden State Warriors a run for their money before losing in 7 games in the first round.

However, I didn't hire you to win three playoff games, I hired you to win 16 of them. You're fired!

You're journey has ended.
Enjoy being an armchair GM.

Words of Wisdom:

When you face a crisis, you know who your true friends are.

- Magic Johnson

Lakers Owner Jim Buss: *Emeka Okafor was the right back-up center to sign in my opinion. I'm extremely excited about this signing!*

I remember watching Emeka dominate at UConn and lead them to the NCAA Title in 2004. The kid was just an all-around defensive force and he reminded me of a young Hakeem Olajuwon without the offense. I've been a fan ever since. I even know his real name, did you know that? I bet you don't know Emeka's real name. Are you ready? Wait for it. Emeka's real name is ... Chukwuemeka Ndubuisi Okafor; boom, are you impressed? Oh yeah, I'm the man!

Anyways, I'm thrilled you signed Okafor instead of Matt Bonner or B.J. Mullens. I know Okafor's an injury risk but those other two guys are just so far below him that taking this risk is more than worth it.

You have impressed me every step of the way so far. Now go sign four reserves and get to work on hiring the coach who will lead my team to the title!

Continue on to page 138.

Lakers Owner Jim Buss: *I will state the obvious; signing B.J. Mullens was a big mistake. I thought you were the right man for the job up until the point you signed B.J., which as far as I'm concerned stands for barely-jumps, to be our back-up center. Once you did that I knew your previous successes were a charade and that this would all end horribly; I was right.*

The team you assembled wasn't a bad regular season team. They won 50 games which is a successful year. However, once we entered the playoffs and faced off with the Golden State Warriors we got exposed. We had a shot to go up 2-1 in the series before Pau got hurt and had to be replaced by Mullens who proceeded to shoot us out of that Game 3 and later the entire series. We lost in 5 games and as soon as that fifth game ended your fate was sealed.

You're fired. Now get out!

You're journey has ended.
Enjoy being an armchair GM.

Words of Wisdom:

I can't relate to lazy people. We don't speak the same language. I don't understand you. I don't want to understand you.

- Kobe Bryant

You now have just four roster spots left to fill and need a third-string point guard, shooting guard, small forward and power forward. After scouring the market for the best players possible who will also accept minimum contracts, there are three solid options available to you.

The first option is to bring back four of last season's Lakers: Jodie Meeks, Kent Bazemore, Xavier Henry and Ryan Kelly.

All four of the above players would provide youth, athleticism and scoring punch off the bench. You would also know what you're getting as all four have played for the Lakers and none are known to be high-maintenance.

The second option is to sign four former all-stars: Stephon Marbury, Chauncey Billups, Tracy McGrady and Kenyon Martin.

All four of the above players have big names and Hollywood loves big names, no doubt about that. Martin is a former number one draft pick, McGrady is a former multi-time scoring champ, Marbury was known as Starbury during his heyday and Billups is known as *Mr. Big Shot* and has an *NBA Finals MVP* trophy on his resume. However, only Billups and Martin played in the league last year and neither had a solid season. Signing these four players is a classic high-risk high-reward dilemma.

The third option is to sign four of the best street-ballers on the planet today: Patrick Robinson aka *Pat the Roc*, Hugh Jones aka *Baby Shaq*, Anthony Pimble aka *Mr. Afrika* and Renaldo Johnson aka *Violator.*

All four of the above players would bring an incredible amount of energy and athleticism to the team, not to mention entertainment and everyone knows Lakers fans love to be entertained. Robinson played for the Cincinnati Bearcats when he was 5'9" and amazingly grew to 6'2" after leaving college and his game has grown with him. Pimble won back-to-back conference titles at Ventura Community College in California and is known for his insane dunking ability. Johnson has played professionally overseas for seven years and is known for his lock-down defense. Jones is perhaps the best known player and someone many, including Shaquille O'Neal, think should have been in the NBA years ago. You can learn more about these players at the **www.ballup.com** website.

If you would like to sign Meeks, Bazemore, Henry and Kelly,
turn to page 140.

If you would like to sign Marbury, Billups, McGrady and Martin,
turn to page 141.

If you would like to sign Robinson, Jones, Pimble and Johnson,
turn to page 142.

Lakers Owner Jim Buss: *I hope you made the right call this time. I love the team as-is and am very happy to have Jodie Meeks, Kent Bazemore, Xavier Henry and Ryan Kelly back. In fact, I'm shocked you were able to get Jodie back on a minimum contract. To think that just a short while ago you called his bluff and refused to give him the loot he was asking for and are now getting him for the minimum is just awesome. It's a testament to your shrewd negotiating as well as Jodie's love for the Lakers and dedication to winning here in L.A.*

As far as I can see, our team is set. The roster is loaded and I can't wait for the first game of the season!

You've done a great job so far but don't get complacent. We may have a nice roster but without a top-notch coach things could fall apart quickly. So get your butt to work and find me the next ring-winning Lakers coach now!

Continue on to page 143.

Lakers Owner Jim Buss: *Signing former All-Stars Stephon Marbury, Chauncey Billups, Tracy McGrady and Kenyon Martin was a risky move. Every single one of them played solid basketball individually and put up decent per minute stats but chemistry was always an issue and ended up costing us big-time.*

We got off to a rough start going 10-8 to start the season but finished on a high note winning 55 games and earning the fourth seed in the Western Conference. We even knocked off the Golden State Warriors in the first round which had me dreaming of another title. However, in the second round we ran into the Thunder and then they ran us out of the gym. The former all-stars you signed couldn't keep up with the Thunder's young legs and took out their frustrations on their own teammates. It was a disaster.

I didn't hire you to witness a disaster. You're fired!

You're journey has ended.
Enjoy being an armchair GM.

Words of Wisdom:

Love is the force that ignites the spirit and binds teams together.

- Phil Jackson

Lakers Owner Jim Buss: *Who would have guessed that signing four street ballers would turn out to be a bad decision? Um, only every NBA executive on the planet other than you!*

I know the fans were clamoring for you to sign the guys from the Ball Up squad as fans love to see sick dunks and crazy passes and all that but you can't take instructions from the fans. Many of them never even played organized basketball!

It's also not as if the guys you signed were Joe 'the Destroyer' Hammond, Earl 'the Goat' Manigault, Rick 'Pee Wee' Kirkland and Ed 'Booger' Smith. Had you signed those guys in their primes you wouldn't be in my office right now, you'd be at a championship parade. But you didn't sign those guys did you? No!

We may have snuck into the playoffs as an eight seed but we were also the laughing stock of the league this year and led the NBA in turnovers! Getting swept by the Thunder in the first round was the final nail in your coffin. You're fired!

You're journey has ended.
Enjoy being an armchair GM.

Words of Wisdom:

Don't let other people tell you what you want.

- Pat Riley

Lakers 2014-15 Roster

After filling your final roster spots with former Lakers, your Los Angeles Lakers 2014-15 roster is set and looks as follows:

Starting Point Guard:	Kendall Marshall	$915,243
Starting Shooting Guard:	Kobe Bryant	$23,500,000
Starting Small Forward:	Trevor Ariza	$6,557,377
Starting Power Forward:	Julius Randle	$2,997,360
Starting Center:	Pau Gasol	$8,372,094
Backup Point Guard:	Jordan Farmar	$1,227,985
Backup Shooting Guard:	Gordon Hayward	$11,113,339
Backup Small Forward:	World Peace	$1,448,490
Backup Power Forward:	Channing Frye	$6,800,000
Backup Center:	Emeka Okafor	$1,448,490
Reserve Point Guard:	Jodie Meeks	$1,063,384
Reserve Shooting Guard:	Kent Bazemore	$915,243
Reserve Small Forward:	Xavier Henry	$981,084
Reserve Power Forward:	Ryan Kelly	$816,482
Reserve Center:	Robert Sacre	$915,243
Total Team Salary:		$69,071,814

With the roster set and training camp about to start in less than six weeks, it is high time you decided who to hire and who will coach your team to glory. Choose wisely.

HIRING A COACH

As all basketball fans should know, let alone an NBA General Manager, a coach can literally mean the difference between a team ending up in the draft lottery and a team ending up having a championship parade at the end of the season. The San Antonio Spurs have rarely had one of the top rosters *on paper* yet year in and year out Coach Gregg Popovich has them near the top of the standings. The 2003-04 Detroit Pistons weren't projected by even their most ardent supporters to win a championship yet Coach Larry Brown led a team without even one bona fide superstar to an improbable finals victory over a star-studded Lakers squad that featured four future Hall-of-Famers (Kobe

Bryant, Shaquille O'Neal, Karl Malone and Gary Payton) that season. Simply put, a great coach can turn a mere contender into a champion. Likewise, a poor coach can turn a legitimate contender into a pretender.

After hiring the mistake that was Mike No-D'Antoni and refusing to hand over control of the franchise to Phil Jackson (which by the way almost led Kobe to having Jim Buss kidnapped and fed to the shark he was swimming with in that Turkish Airlines commercial), Jim Buss is counting on you to hire the coach that will return this great franchise to glory. Don't let him down.

There are four coaches you are interested in and who you know would love to coach the roster you've assembled. They are: George Karl, Byron Scott, Kareem Abdul-Jabbar and Jeff Van Gundy.

George Karl: One of the winningest coaches in league history. The 63 year old who loves to run, run and run some more on the offensive end last coached during the 2012-13 season when he won Coach of the Year. Karl compiled a career win/loss record of 1,131-756 for a .599 winning percentage and won one Conference Championship in 25 seasons while also leading three separate franchises (Seattle, Milwaukee and Denver) to Conference Finals appearances.

However, Karl also went 8-16 in the playoffs during his last four seasons in Denver, failed to get out of the first round even one time, supposedly lost his locker-room, and later uncouthly criticized his former star player Carmelo Anthony after Anthony was traded to the New York Knicks. There is concern that Karl may not mesh with Kobe Bryant and that his up-tempo style of basketball may not be the right fit for the Lakers current roster.

Byron Scott: 2007-08 NBA Coach of the Year. The 53 year old former Laker star shooting guard last coached during the 2012-13 season, compiled a .579 playoff winning percentage and won 2 Conference Championships in 13 seasons.

However, Scott also compiled a rather poor career regular season win/loss record of 416-521 for a .444 winning percentage. There are also concerns that while he may get along fine with Kobe Bryant, he may not be the right coach for young players such as Julius Randle, Kendall Marshall, Xavier Henry and the like due to his *my way or the highway* approach to coaching.

Kareem Abdul-Jabbar: The undisputed G.O.A.T. (Greatest of All Time) of college basketball, the disputed G.O.A.T. of the NBA as well as the league's all-time leading scorer, six-time MVP and six time champion. The 67 year old former Laker is known as an extremely intelligent individual with a magnificent basketball I.Q.

However, Abdul-Jabbar is also known as a very surly character that can be incredibly hard to get along with. Such may be the single most important reason *Mr. Skyhook* has never been offered a head coaching position to date.

Jeff Van Gundy: Jeff Van Gundy is the son of former Brockport State University head coach Bill Van Gundy and brother of Detroit Pistons President of Basketball Operations and Head Coach Stan Van Gundy.

Van Gundy is known as a defensive guru and tireless worker. The 52 year old current ESPN broadcaster compiled a career win/loss record of 430-318 for a .575 winning percentage, led his team to the playoffs in nine of his ten full seasons and advanced to back-to-back Conference Finals while coaching the Knicks. He also led the only eighth seed in NBA history to the Finals in 1998-99 after losing franchise star Patrick Ewing to a season-ending injury during the regular season, and with the best player on the roster most likely being Latrell Sprewell. That's right, Latrell *shut your mouth or I'll choke you* Sprewell!

However, while it's obvious that Jeff is an amazing coach and defensive savant, he is also extremely outspoken and seems to live by personally held principles rather than by league dogma or any particular team owner's own rules. There is therefore concern that Van Gundy may be a little too tough to rein in and a little too outspoken with the media. Choose wisely.

If you would like to offer George Karl a three year $15,000,000 contract,
turn to page 149.

If you would like to offer Byron Scott a three year $12,000,000 contract,
turn to page 150.

If you would like to offer Kareem Abdul-Jabbar a one year $2,000,000 contract,
turn to page 151.

If you would like to offer Jeff Van Gundy a three year $18,000,000 contract,
turn to page 152.

Lakers Owner Jim Buss: *Offering George Karl a three year $15,000,000 contract was a solid decision. Karl led us to 63 wins and the top seed in the Western Conference which was great. Then we swept Mark Cuban's Mavericks in the first round, crushed Dwight Coward's Rockets 4-1 in the second round and slapped around should-have-been-Laker Chris Paul and Donald Sterling's Paper-Clips in the Western Conference Finals. I was on cloud nine!*

However when we ran into LeBron and the Cavs in the NBA Finals everything changed. Karl never adjusted to the Cavs speed at all. LeBron and Kyrie Irving went wild on us and while Karl could have switched Ariza onto Kyrie and doubled LeBron with Kobe and Metta, and while he should have had the team play at a much slower pace, he did neither. We lost 4-1 and therefore you should have hired a different coach as I didn't hire you to merely get me to the Finals but the win them!

Get out of my office. You're fired!

You're journey has ended.
Enjoy being an armchair GM.

Words of Wisdom:

There's no such thing as coulda, shoulda, or woulda. If you shoulda and coulda, you woulda done it.

- Pat Riley

Lakers Owner Jim Buss: *Offering Byron Scott a three year $12,000,000 contract was a solid decision. Scott led the Lakers to a 55-27 record and the third seed in the Western Conference which had me dreaming of another title before the playoffs started.*

However, everything started to go wrong the second we stepped onto the court against the Spurs in the first round of the playoffs. I should have figured as much when the Spurs lost their final game on purpose to avoid playing the Clippers, preferring to play us instead.

I believe you built a roster that could have won that series but after we lost the first game on a last second basket, off a play that Gregg Popovich drew up to perfection, it was as if Byron Scott knew he couldn't outcoach Popovich and just gave up on the series. You built a great roster but you hired the wrong coach and now you're fired! Get out of my office!

You're journey has ended.
Enjoy being an armchair GM.

Words of Wisdom:

Giving yourself permission to lose guarantees a loss.

- Pat Riley

Lakers Owner Jim Buss: *Hiring Kareem Abdul-Jabbar was a risky decision, yet he exceeded everyone's expectations this season, everyone's except mine that is. The Captain led us to 57 wins and a quick 5 game series victory over the Timberwolves, followed by a 6 game series victory over should-have-been-Laker Chris Paul and the Paper-Clips. I was really excited by that point; then reality set in.*

When we drew the Oklahoma City Thunder in the Conference Finals, I knew it was over. While the players respected and responded to Abdul-Jabbar his lack of experience cost them game seven when he inadvertently picked up a technical after a shooting foul had been called on Kobe Bryant with just 7 seconds left in the game and the Lakers down one. Russell Westbrook sank both free throws and Kevin Durant hit the technical giving the Thunder an insurmountable four point lead and the Conference title.

You should never have hired a first-time coach. You had a good run but it's done and so are you. You're fired!

You're journey has ended.
Enjoy being an armchair GM.

Words of Wisdom:

You can't win unless you learn how to lose.

- Kareem Abdul-Jabbar

Lakers Owner Jim Buss: *You got Jeff Van Gundy? Yeah baby, yeah! This is the best news I've had since hearing about the Tupac Shakur sighting in Maseru, Lesotho. Turns out he was living in seclusion in Cuba since his vanishing in 1996 and eventually made his way to South Africa before settling in Maseru, Lesotho. I guess he's got a couple of wives (polygamy is legal there) and six children there and the locals know him as the 'thothokiso moromuwa' which means poet missionary. Isn't that awesome?*

California, no doubt about it, California, no doubt about it; in the city of L.A., whoo! I am so geeked! The seven day theory was real, Tupac is alive and my Lakers are going to be coached by an awesome coach again; life is good!

Coach Van Gundy should do wonders with the defense. I also love that he's fiery and speaks his mind as that will play great with the media here.

Hopefully you won't have to do much of anything except watch the victories pile up. However, we are a little short on star power and you might need to work your magic and pull off a trade if things don't go well.

Continue on to page 153.

THE MID-WAY POINT

At the mid-way point of the season and thanks in large part to the best bench in the NBA by far, your Lakers sit firmly atop the Western Conference and a full game ahead of the second place Oklahoma City Thunder. A Conference Finals appearance seems like a foregone conclusion if the team can stay healthy, yet a title may still be a long-shot, thanks to LeBron James and his dominant Cleveland Cavaliers.

Over in the Eastern Conference, the Cavaliers, sparked by the return of Akron, Ohio's own LeBron James and the magnificent play of number one draft pick

Joel Embiid, have been steamrolling through their opposition. The Cavs have a full six game lead on the Indiana Pacers for the best record in the East and a four game lead on the Lakers for the best record in the NBA.

It was shocking news when LeBron James decided to opt out of the final year of his contract with the Miami Heat and re-join the team that drafted him, especially after Cavs owner Dan Gilbert went all *Adolf* and publicly denounced James for leaving. However, the man known as *King James* was never stupid. He showed his basketball intelligence when he signed with the Heat and then went out and won multiple titles, and he showed it again this past summer when he left the aging Heat to sign with a Cavs team loaded with young talent and another legit superstar with his best days ahead of him in Kyrie Irving. And now, LeBron is once again reaping the rewards of his prudent basketball decision-making.

While your Lakers are rolling in the West, you may need to make a small change or two to assure yourself a title this season, as as-is the team has the look of a Western Conference champion, though perhaps not an NBA champion. That said, don't be afraid to rock the boat if need be as your future as Lakers GM may depend on you doing so.

If the playoffs were to begin today each Conference's top eight seeds would look as follows:

Western Conference

1. Los Angeles Lakers
2. Houston Rockets
3. Oklahoma City Thunder
4. Golden State Warriors
5. Los Angeles Clippers
6. San Antonio Spurs
7. Minnesota Timberwolves
8. Dallas Mavericks

Eastern Conference

1. Cleveland Cavaliers
2. Indiana Pacers
3. Chicago Bulls
4. Brooklyn Nets
5. Toronto Raptors
6. Washington Wizards
7. Detroit Pistons
8. Miami Heat

Several Lakers are embedded in the various individual trophy races as well. Kobe Bryant seems like a shoe-in to win the *Most Improved Player* award though Derick Rose is certainly a strong second. Bryant also has an outside shot at winning his second MVP award as well, thanks in large part to the team's fantastic record and his 25.1 points per game which is fifth highest in the league.

Julius Randle is in a four way race for the *Rookie of the Year* award along with Andrew Wiggins, Jabari Parker and Joel Embiid. However, seeing as Randle is scoring more than any rookie not named Andrew or Jabari and averaging more rebounds than any rookie not named Embiid, and especially seeing as Randle will most likely be the only one of the four to make the playoffs, he may just be the favorite to win R.O.Y.

Gordon Hayward is also leading the pack for the *6th Man of the Year* award thanks to his magnificent all-around play. Hayward is averaging 13.1 points, 5.2 rebounds, 5.1 assists and 1.3 steals in 33 minutes per game while also shooting career highs in field goal and three-point percentage.

Coach Jeff Van Gundy is also one of the top candidates for *Coach of the Year* along with Kevin McHale and magician Gregg Popovich who has the Spurs in the thick of the playoff race despite Tony Parker, Manu Ginobili and Tim Duncan all missing extended time with injuries this season. However the Cleveland Cavaliers John Calipari seems to be the front-runner as his Cavaliers have captured the attention of everyone, including the voters.

At this point of the season LeBron James has a firm grip on the *MVP* trophy thanks to completely transforming the Cleveland Cavaliers from a laughing-stock into a juggernaut almost over-night. However, defending MVP Kevin Durant, thanks in large part to his league-leading 31.8 points per game is also a strong candidate, while Minnesota's Kevin Love is a serious dark-horse candidate as he is not only leading the league in rebounds but is third in scoring and has the Timberwolves firmly in line to make the playoffs for the first time in 11 seasons.

Anthony Davis of the New Orleans Pelicans also seems to have a stranglehold on the *Defensive Player of the Year* award, though LeBron James may get his fair share of votes for that award as well. Rajon Rondo is leading the league in assists as well, with Chris Paul and Ricky Rubio tied for second in that category.

ALL-STAR WEEKEND

The Western and Eastern Conference All-Star rosters this season are as follows:

Western Conference

Coach:	Jeff Van Gundy
Starting Guard:	Chris Paul
Starting Guard:	Kobe Bryant
Starting Forward:	Kevin Durant
Starting Forward:	Kevin Love
Starting Forward:	Blake Griffin
Backup Guard:	Russell Westbrook
Backup Guard:	James Harden
Backup Forward:	LaMarcus Aldridge
Backup Forward:	Anthony Davis
Backup Forward:	DeMarcus Cousins
Reserve:	Stephen Curry
Reserve:	Dirk Nowitzki

Eastern Conference

Coach:	John Calipari
Starting Guard:	Derrick Rose
Starting Guard:	Kyrie Irving
Starting Forward:	Paul George
Starting Forward:	Carmelo Anthony
Starting Forward:	LeBron James
Backup Guard:	John Wall
Backup Guard:	Dwyane Wade
Backup Forward:	Chris Bosh
Backup Forward:	Joakim Noah
Backup Forward:	Al Jefferson
Reserve:	Rajon Rondo
Reserve:	Andre Drummond

Kobe Bryant was the only member of the Lakers to make the All-Star team this season. However, the team was also coached by Jeff Van Gundy and the West beat the East 132-128 behind an MVP performance from the Black Mamba himself, who uncharacteristically buried nine three pointers en route to 33 points in the contest.

You are now ready for the second half of the NBA season. The trade deadline is also rapidly approaching and you may wish to make a trade or two. However if you do so, make sure it actually improves the team as what you have at present is quite special and in line to win the Western Conference.

TRADE DEADLINE

Led by the efficient scoring of Kobe Bryant, solid post play of Pau Gasol, flashes of dominance from Julius Randle, magnificent bench play and inspired coaching, the Lakers have lost just 11 games all season. However, four of those losses have come in their last seven games, to the likes of the Thunder, Clippers and Rockets as well as a blow-out loss at the hands of the Cavaliers. The Lakers now trail the Oklahoma City Thunder by 1.5 games and have even lost the Pacific Division lead to the Clippers who sit 1.0 game ahead of them in the standings thanks to a nine game win streak. The Cleveland Cavaliers, led by LeBron James and Kyrie Irving, have continued to steamroll the competition and now have a full 7.0 game lead on the Lakers for the best record in the NBA.

The good news is that not one single player on the Lakers roster has been a disappointment to date, while Julius Randle, Kendall Marshall and Gordon Hayward have far exceeded expectations. Randle is leading the team in rebounds at 10.1 per game and is fourth in the entire league (behind only Andre Drummond, Deandre Jordan and Kevin Love) in rebounds per 48 minutes. Marshall's offensive efficiency and masterful ball handling have been better than ever and his attention to detail and obvious effort on the defensive end (though Kendall would still never be confused with a great defender at the point guard position) has been impressive as well. Hayward has been the Lakers jack-of-all-trades and first man off the bench and has also consistently been on the floor in crunch time all season long.

However, if there has been one single player that has seemed to be a harbinger of whether the Lakers will win or lose a particular game based on his individual play, it has far and away been rookie Julius Randle. Randle has taken on the role of garbage man on this team, rebounding like a mad man, scoring on put-backs and tip-ins and doing all the dirty work necessary for the team to be successful. He has also become the team's primary offensive weapon when Kobe Bryant and Pau Gasol need to rest and has earned himself the reputation of enforcer as well after tossing Blake Griffin to the ground shortly after Griffin delivered a seemingly unnecessary hard foul on Kobe Bryant, earlier this season,. Julius *A Lot to Handle* Randle has lived up to the nickname legendary street-ball entrepreneur Bobbito Garcia gave him as he has definitely been a lot to handle for his opponents.

However, despite all of Randle's obvious gifts and maniacal drive to succeed, he has, like most rookies, been wildly inconsistent. This inconsistency was never more evident than in back-to-back games against the San Antonio Spurs and Dallas Mavericks earlier this season. Generally speaking, most players play much better in the first game of a back-to-back. However, in the first game against the Spurs Randle was absolutely shut down by the legendary but aging Tim Duncan. While Duncan went off for 27 points and 17 rebounds in 36 minutes Randle was held to just 7 points and 4 rebounds in the same amount of time. Yet in the second game against the Mavericks who were starting Dirk

Nowitzki and undersized Dejuan Blair in the front-court Randle erupted for 31 points and 20 rebounds and simply could not be contained.

An over-simplified statement would be that Randle is able to score and rebound at will against poor or under-sized defenders while he can seem to disappear when matched up against great or even merely long and lengthy defenders and that such could be a problem come playoff time, let alone in a Conference Finals or NBA Finals matchup against the likes of Serge Ibaka or LeBron James. However, the real truth is that Randle is simply inconsistent and while his energy level seems to run high at all times and while none of his coaches or teammates question his effort or desire to win at all costs, he is a rookie and rookies are inconsistent, period.

Randle has also been dealing with a mildly sprained ankle and sore right shoulder which could explain, along with the mythological *rookie-wall*, his dip in production since the mid-way point of the season. However, the training staff doesn't believe such injuries are serious or that they will cause him to miss any extended time.

All of the above said, there are now just 24 hours left until the trade deadline passes. As the Lakers are not in the dreaded *Luxury Tax* you have the ability to acquire incoming salaries that are up to 150% plus $100,000 more than the salaries of the players you trade, if the salaries of the players you trade are under $9,800,000 (Ex: If you trade players that make $2,000,000 you may receive players that make up to $3,100,000 in salary). If the salaries of the players you are trading are greater than $9,800,000 you may receive players with salaries up to $5,000,000 higher than the combined salaries of what you are trading away (Ex: If you trade players that make $10,000,000 you may receive players that make up $15,000,000 in salary). However, you are just $7,928,186 shy of the luxury tax threshold so while you don't have to worry about making one trade that adds $5,000,000 in salary, you must realize that you cannot complete two trades that add anything more than $7,928,186 in salary. Simply put, you have options and options are always a good thing.

At this point you have let each and every GM across the league know that you are *open for business*, going all-in to a win a championship this season and that you will consider any trade that will give the Lakers a better shot to win a ring this season. Various General Managers across the league have already let you know in no uncertain terms that they have no desire to help you in your quest and will not be submitting any trade proposals to you whatsoever. Phil Jackson himself even let Jim Buss know that he would only consider making any sort of trade with you, if Jim personally submitted a public apology to the Los Angeles Times, apologizing for not giving Phil *whatever he wanted*; of course there's a better chance JaMarcus Russell comes out of retirement and leads the Raiders to a Super Bowl victory than such an apology being issued!

Many other GM's submitted at least one trade proposal to you which you rejected out of hand as they were laughable and would have only served to decrease your chances of winning a title this season. There are three trade proposals that you feel merit serious consideration though, any one or more of which you could choose to pull the trigger on. However, please be aware that these trade decisions are the last move(s) you will make roster-wise that will directly affect the team's on-court performance this season.

You can choose to stand pat and trust the team you have assembled so far and see what the Coach Van Gundy can do with such a roster. Or, you can pull the trigger on one of the following three trade proposals. Choose wisely.

Proposal One: Portland Trail Blazers General Manager Neil Olshey has offered to trade LaMarcus Aldridge and his $15,200,000 expiring contract for Gordon Hayward who earns $11,113,339, Julius Randle who earns $2,997,360 and Kendall Marshall with his $915,243 expiring contract.

Proposal Two: Boston Celtics General Manager Danny Ainge (after hearing from Rajon Rondo's agent that Rondo will be testing free agency this summer and has no interest in signing with the Celtics unless they severly over-pay for his services) has offered to trade Rajon Rondo and his $13,000,000 expiring contract as well as 24 year old reserve guard/forward Chris Johnson who earns $915,000 this season (and has team options for the following two seasons) for Gordon Hayward who earns $11,113,339, Kendall Marshall and his $915,243 expiring contract and a future unprotected first round draft pick.

Proposal Three: Detroit Pistons General Manager Joe Dumars has offered to trade Josh Smith who will earn $14,000,000 per season through 2016-17 along with Chauncey Billups and his $2,500,000 expiring contract for Gordon Hayward who earns $11,113,339 and Julius Randle who earns $2,997,360.

If you would like to stand pat,
turn to page 165.

If you would like to trade Hayward, Randle and Marshall to the Trailblazers for LaMarcus Aldridge,
turn to page 166.

If you would like to trade Hayward, Marshall and a future unprotected first round draft pick to the Boston Celtics for Rajon Rondo and Christapher Johnson,
turn to page 167.

If you would like to trade Hayward and Randle to the Detroit Pistons for Josh Smith and Chauncey Billups,
turn to page 168.

Lakers Owner Jim Buss: *You had the ability to trade for Rajon Rondo and didn't. I knew when that happened you didn't have what it takes to win a ring.*

We finished up with a 54-28 record and earned the fourth seed in the Western Conference. However we couldn't even make it out of the first round of the playoffs and the Golden State Warriors embarrassed us. Steph Curry went gonzo and made Kendall Marshall look like his feet were stuck in cement. It was as if Marshall was scared to be a leader, to step up and accept the challenge Curry was throwing at him. Curry torched Marshall to the tune of 38 points per game and we got knocked out in just 5 games.

I think it's obvious Rajon Rondo would have done wonders for our team but you didn't have the guts to pull the trigger. You're fired!

You're journey has ended.
Enjoy being an armchair GM.

Words of Wisdom:

I've always been a leader my whole life. I've always led. I didn't know how to do anything else.

-Magic Johnson

Lakers Owner Jim Buss: *When you traded two starters and our jack-of-all-trades in Gordon Hayward who plays starter type minutes for LaMarcus Aldridge I cringed. I'm an Aldridge fan and the guy was obviously more ready for playoff basketball than a rookie like Julius Randle was, but giving up three players that played over 100 combined minutes per game for one player who plays less than 40 minutes? Not smart, not smart at all.*

With Aldridge forming a devastating frontcourt pairing with Pau Gasol we stormed to a 63-19 record and the top seed in the Western Conference. We even swept the Mavericks in the first round which had me thinking championship. However, Dwight Coward's Rockets knocked us out in 6 games in the second round thanks in large part to our lack of depth. I blame you for that.

You're fired; get out of my office!

You're journey has ended.
Enjoy being an armchair GM.

Words of Wisdom:

You can never have enough talent.

- Pat Riley

Lakers Owner Jim Buss: *You got Rondo? I'm almost speechless. I mean, on one hand I can't stand the little alien but on the other hand I know full well he might be the best all-around pure point guard on the planet.*

Regardless, I'd rather win a ring with Rondo than a mere conference title with Kendall Marshall and Gordon Hayward and I think we can definitely win a ring with Rondo steering our ship! Losing both Marshall and Hayward hurts but you've got to give up something good to get something good.

I really think Hayward can become an All-Star in this league and that Marshall will be a solid point guard for many years. However, if I'm being honest with myself, I'm not sure either player was ready to win a title this year. And, I'm positive that neither one was anywhere near as ready to lead a team to a title as Rajon Rondo is, that's for sure!

I guess what I'm trying to say is, great job! Keep up the good work!

Continue on to page 169.

Lakers Owner Jim Buss: *What is wrong with you? I'm serious; answer my question; what in the world is wrong with you?*

You went from a hero to a zero in the span of a couple of hours. You built a great roster and then destroyed it, and for what, the most moody guy in the NBA in Josh Smith and a guy who should be coaching rather than playing at this stage of his career in Chauncey Billups? You disgust me!

You could've got Rondo and upgraded our point guard position which is what we needed, but instead you traded away a future All-Star in Julius Randle and this year's 6th Man of the Year in Gordon Hayward for Josh 'J-Grumpy' Smith and Chauncey 'Mr. No Shot' Billups? Insanity!

You've obviously lost your mind and now you've lost your job. You're fired!

You're journey has ended.
Enjoy being an armchair GM.

Words of Wisdom:

Great effort springs naturally from great attitude.

- Pat Riley

After trading Gordon Hayward and Kendall Marshall for Rajon Rondo and Christopher Johnson, your team salary is now at $70,958,232. This said, you are now just $6,041,768 under the luxury tax threshold.

The trade deadline is nearing an end and Jim Buss is thrilled with your roster as-is. However, you just received two phone calls that have you thinking and thinking hard.

The first call was from Memphis Grizzlies General Manager Chris Wallace. Wallace has offered to trade you Pau Gasol's 30 year old little brother Marc and his $15,829,688 expiring contract for Julius Randle, Channing Frye and Emeka Okafor who combine to earn $11,245,850 this season.

The second call was from Minnesota Timberwolves President of Basketball Operations Flip Saunders. Saunders was recently informed by Kevin Love's agent Jeff Schwartz that Love will not be exercising his team option for the 2015-16 season and will in fact be signing with either the Los Angeles Lakers or New York Knicks this summer. Saunders is scared to death to lose Love for nothing the way the Orlando Magic lost Shaquille O'Neal in the summer of 96' and the Lakers lost Dwight Howard in the summer of 13' and is therefore offering to trade Kevin Love and his $15,719,063 expiring contract and undrafted rookie Deandre Kane and his $507,336 expiring contract for Julius Randle, Channing Frye Robert Sacre and Kent Bazemore who combine to earn $11,627,846 this season, along with $3,000,000 cash.

The third call was from Knicks Grand Poobah Phil Jackson. Jackson said that he would let bygones be bygones, forgive and forget and all that good stuff if you would trade Julius Randle and Channing Frye, who combine to earn $9,797,360 for Tyson Chandler and his $14,596,888 expiring contract, as well as Iman Shumpert and his $2,761,113 expiring contract, as according to the *Zen Master,* such would help both teams immensely.

You have a very important decision to make. You could choose to stand pat with a starting lineup of Rajon Rondo, Kobe Bryant, Trevor Ariza, Julius Randle and Pau Gasol along with solid depth at every position. You could also choose to make a 3-for-1 trade to acquire Pau's little brother Marc Gasol in the hopes that such a trade will not only increase team chemistry but improve your front-court for a title run. You could even make a 3-for-1 trade for MVP candidate Kevin Love and hope that he will be the perfect complement to the current Rajon Rondo, Kobe Bryant, Pau Gasol *Big 3*. Choose wisely.

If you would like to stand pat,
turn to page 171.

If you would like to trade Randle, Frye and Okafor to the
Grizzlies for Marc Gasol,
turn to page 172.

If you would like to trade Randle, Frye and Sacre to the
Timberwolves for Kevin Love,
turn to page 173.

If you would like to trade Randle and Frye to the Knicks for
Tyson Chandler and Iman Shumpert,
turn to page 174.

Lakers Owner Jim Buss: *You believed in the roster you had built and stood pat and I respected that. We even finished the year on a tear and earned the third seed in the Western Conference.*

However, we drew the San Antonio Spurs in the first round and they drew first blood, winning Game One on a buzzer-beater by Tim Duncan, who was planning to retire at the end of the season. We fought our way to a seventh game but the Spurs and their 'win-one-for-Duncan' mantra was too much to overcome.

The Spurs knocked my team out of the playoffs and in turn they knocked you out of your job. You're fired!

You're journey has ended.
Enjoy being an armchair GM.

Words of Wisdom:

If you're afraid to fail, then you're probably going to fail.

- Kobe Bryant

Lakers Owner Jim Buss: *Trading for Marc Gasol improved the team dramatically. With the Gasol brothers forming perhaps the most multi-skilled post duo in league history we steamrolled to a 64-18 record and the top seed in the Western Conference; we even won the West, sweeping the Mavericks, knocking the Rockets out in five and hammering the Thunder 4-2 in the Conference Finals. However, the NBA Finals were a different beast altogether.*

The Cleveland Cavaliers had just finished breezing through the East, winning 16 games and losing just two. We played them tough, winning games one, four and six and forcing a seventh game back in Cleveland. However, in the first quarter of the deciding game, LeBron drove the lane and hammered a hard dunk right on Marc Gasol's head. From that point on it was if LeBron felt like he could do whatever he wanted. We lost.

You accomplished more than most would have, I realize that ... but, you're still fired!

You're journey has ended.
Enjoy being an armchair GM.

Words of Wisdom:

You have to defeat a great player's aura more than his game.

- Pat Riley

Lakers Owner Jim Buss: *I can't believe this; Kevin Love is a Laker! Jack Kent Cooke had Wilt Chamberlain and Jerry West. My dad had Magic and Kareem. Jerry West brought Kobe and Shaq together. Mitch Kupchak united Pau Gasol with Kobe Bryant. However you, you have brought Rajon Rondo and Kevin Love to Los Angeles to play with Kobe and Pau; that is unbelievable, just unbelievable!*

Words can't even express how insanely ecstatic I am right now. If MVP voters didn't ridiculously factor in team success into their choice, Kevin Love would have finished 3rd in the MVP race last year. The guy is a superstar who has gotten better every single year he's been in the league. He came into the NBA as a chubby big man who rebounded like mad and is now the most deadly stretch-4 the game has ever seen and still rebounds like mad. He's also known as an incredibly hard worker who will do whatever it takes to win. The guy is just a stud and now he's a Lakers stud, woo-hoo!

Great job! If I wouldn't have given you the title or bust ultimatum I would lock you up to a long-term contract right now. However, I did give you the title or bust ultimatum and I definitely expect a title now that we have K-Love. Now get out of here and bring the trophy back to the Staples Center where it belongs!

Continue on to page 175.

Author Bryant T. Jordan: *That would have been a great trade huh? Nabbing both Tyson Chandler and Iman Shumpert for Randle and Frye and Joel Anthony seemed like a no-brainer didn't it.*

However, choosing this option simply proves you don't have what it takes to be an NBA General Manager as you obviously have a problem paying attention to detail. I made it very clear that the absolute maximum you could take back in additional salary was $6,041,768. Now, you tell me what $14,596,888 (Tyson Chandler's salary) plus $2,761,113 (Iman Shumpert's salary) is? That's right, it's $17,358,001.

Now, you tell me what $17,358,001 minus $9,797,360 (the combined outgoing salaries of Sullinger, Frye and Anthony) is? That's right again, it's $7,560,641.

Now, you tell me if $7,560,641 is more or less than $6,041,768? That's right again, it's more, which means you just tried to execute a trade that isn't even possible under the current CBA!

I'm not Lakers Owner Jim Buss so I won't fire you. You can go back to Page 172 and try again, but this time, check those digits baby! And, by the way, go buy a copy of my 'Saving the Celtics: A Be the General Manager Book' as well. I could use the loot.

Words of Wisdom:

Check those digits baby!

- Bryant T. Jordan

THE FRUITS OF YOUR LABOR

Your Los Angeles Lakers 2014-15 roster is now 13 deep, set in stone, and as follows:

Starting Point Guard:	Rajon Rondo	$13,000,000
Starting Shooting Guard:	Kobe Bryant	$23,500,000
Starting Small Forward:	Trevor Ariza	$6,557,377
Starting Power Forward:	Kevin Love	$15,719,063
Starting Center:	Pau Gasol	$8,372,094
Backup Point Guard:	Jordan Farmar	$1,227,985
Backup Shooting Guard:	Jodie Meeks	$1,063,384
Backup Small Forward:	World Peace	$1,448,490
Backup Power Forward:	Ryan Kelly	$816,482
Backup Center:	Emeka Okafor	$1,448,490
11th Man:	Xavier Henry	$981,084
12th Man:	DeAndre Kane	$507,336
13th Man:	Christ. Johnson	$915,243
Total Team Salary:		$75,557,028

After making the gutsy decisions to trade young star Julius Randle, super-sub Gordon Hayward, starting point guard Kendall Marshall, backup power forward Channing Frye , reserve center Robert Sacre, reserve swingman Kent Bazemore and a future first round pick and $3,000,000 cash to acquire all-world point guard Rajon Rondo and MVP candidate Kevin Love, despite already being a top three team in your Conference with a solid chance to win a title, the potential for disaster was huge (especially considering Rajon Rondo isn't exactly known as a great chemistry guy). However, the potential for epic success was also huge and with a title or bust ultimatum, swinging for the fences made more sense than taking ball four and walking it out.

Swapping Kendall Marshall and Gordon Hayward for Rajon Rondo (and little used Chris Johnson) may have reduced the team's depth a bit, however Jodie Meeks was able to step into Gordon Hayward's 6th man slot and provide not only consistent and clutch shooting but a great deal of defensive effort and all-around efficiency as well. As for Rajon Rondo himself, the little *Gremlin* was an absolute revelation. Rondo provided his usual outstanding all-around offensive play; however it was his perimeter defensive presence that had Staples Center fans buzzing and every talking head from LA to Taipei calling your Lakers the odds on favorite to win the West and quite possibly the NBA title.

Swapping Julius Randle, Channing Frye, Robert Sacre and Kent Bazemore for Kevin Love was a no-brainer. Losing Frye and filling his minutes with the inconsistent play of Ryan Kelly made for some interesting times, and losing Julius Randle who could be a better player than Kevin Love in 5 years when Love is past his prime and Randle is just entering his, was extremely tough. However, acquiring Love now, while he is playing the best ball of his career and is a bona fide perennial *MVP* candidate was an absolute no-brainer.

Love provided your Lakers with his usual offensive efficiency and masterful rebounding. He also seemed to pick up an extra *edge* playing and practicing with Metta World Peace and Kobe Bryant. Love's newfound edge was never more evident than in the final game of the regular season against the Oklahoma City Thunder. The winner would earn the top seed in the Western Conference while the loser would get the second seed and a much tougher path to the Finals.

During the fourth quarter of a tie game, Serge Ibaka delivered what appeared to be a blatant elbow to Love's nose on a 3-point attempt. The shot went down, as did the subsequent free-throw, giving your Lakers a four point lead with just 1:45 to go in the game. On the Thunder's next trip down the court Kevin Durant missed a fade-away jumper from the left baseline and Kevin Love hauled down the rebound while sending Ibaka crashing to the floor at the same time. Love then started a fast break himself before passing off to Kobe Bryant on the right wing, who sent a cross court pass to Rajon Rondo, who hit a trailing Kevin Love with a beautiful no-look bounce pass. Love corralled the pass and hit and a difficult double-clutch layup while being flailed at and fouled by Serge Ibaka who had hustled to get back into the play. Love reacted to Ibaka's foul by shoving him to the floor and letting out a primal yell. While Love was hit with a technical, by that time the game was well in hand and your Lakers were on their way to the top seed in the West.

Rondo and Love each played a total of 27 games for your Lakers after being acquired in trade. Rondo averaged 10.1 points, 14.1 assists, 6.0 rebounds and 2.1 steals per game while playing 37.2 minutes per game. Love averaged 23.1 points and 15.1 rebounds while shooting a remarkable .501 from the field despite launching 5.5 three-pointers per game.

With Rajon Rondo running the team's offense from the point guard position as well as being the team's primary perimeter defender night in and night out, and with Kevin Love being featured as the team's option 1b along with Kobe Bryant, your Lakers lost just 4 games after the trade deadline and just two of their final 20 games (one of which was the second to last game of the season which Kobe Bryant and Pau Gasol both sat out simply to get some much needed rest). Needless to say, your Lakers entered the Playoffs with a 67-15 record and as the top seed and team to beat in the Western Conference, while the LeBron James led Cleveland Cavaliers entered the Playoffs as the prohibitive favorite in the Eastern Conference as well.

In the first round of the playoffs your Lakers faced off against the extremely young and ultra-talented New Orleans Pelicans. The Pelicans had entered the playoffs on a hot-streak winning nine of their last 10 games and beating out the Minnesota Timberwolves (who faltered after swapping Kevin Love with Julius

Randle at the trade deadline, despite Randle putting up even better numbers in Minnesota than he had in Los Angeles) for the eighth seed. Third year big man Anthony *Unibrow* Davis was on a tear and playing like a future MVP and that continued in the first round as he utterly dominated his matchup with Pau Gasol. However your Lakers were far too balanced, deep and experienced for the young Pelicans. Led by Kobe Bryant's 24.5 points per game and Kevin Love's 23.5 points and 14.5 rebounds your Lakers swept the Pelicans, outscoring them by an average of 13.0 points per game, thanks to a 113-79 throttling in the fourth and final game.

In other Western Conference first round matchups the second seed Houston Rockets won a tough six game series with the Dallas Mavericks. In the sixth and final game Dwight Howard came up big with 19 points, 19 rebounds and 11 blocked shots while James Harden poured in 33 points to give the Rockets a 116-112 victory over the Mavs who wasted Dirk Nowitzki's virtuoso 47 point performance.

The third seed Oklahoma City Thunder brought a violent end to the career of Tim Duncan who was playing his final season with the San Antonio Spurs. The Thunder destroyed the Spurs, sweeping the series and outscoring them by a total of 64 points. Duncan had little impact on the series averaging just 9.5 points and 6.5 rebounds while Kevin Durant and Russell Westbrook each averaged over 28 points per game for the high-scoring Thunder.

The fourth seed Golden State Warriors and fifth seed Los Angeles Clippers met in what was easily the most entertaining and even matchup of the first round. The series came down to an overtime period in the seventh and final game after Chris Paul hit a step-back jumper over the outstretched hand of Andre Iguodala at the regulation buzzer. However, overtime belonged to Golden State's *Splash Brothers* as Stephen Curry and Klay Thompson each nailed two three- pointers and scored eight points as the Warriors won the deciding game 128-123.

In Eastern Conference first round matchups the top seed of the entire playoffs, the Cleveland Cavaliers, absolutely drubbed the eighth seed Miami Heat in four straight games. LeBron James tortured his former team to the tune of averaging a triple double (27.5 points, 10.5 rebounds and 10.0 assists) while playing lock-down defense on former running mate Dwyane Wade who managed to shoot just 29% from the field for the series.

The second seed Indiana Pacers dismantled the seventh seed Detroit Pistons in four straight games. The Pistons put up a fight in games three and four and Andre Drummond dominated his matchup with Pacers center Roy Hibbert throughout the series. However Paul George, Lance Stephenson and the Pacers depth and experience were far too much for the young Pistons to handle and Indiana cruised to an easy first round victory.

The third seed Chicago Bulls and star point guard Derrick Rose faced off against the sixth seed Washington Wizards and their dynamic backcourt of John Wall and Bradley Beal. Rose, Wall and Beal all played magnificently during the series but it was primarily the unforeseen contributions of second year swingman Otto Porter that kept the series tight for Washington. However, the Bulls experience and dogged team defense coupled with the scoring outbursts of Rose and the all-around excellence of Joakim Noah were too much for the young Wizards to overcome as Chicago won the series in six games.

The fourth seed Brooklyn Nets and fifth seed Toronto Raptors engaged in a heated seven game battle to the finish. The aging Kevin Garnett and Paul Pierce led the Nets attack emotionally while Brook Lopez paced the team in scoring. The Raptors however were the superior team. Led by the point mastery of Kyle Lowry, all-around play of DeMar DeRozan, magnificent long-distance bombing of Terrence Ross, hustle of Amir Johnson and post defense and rebounding of Jonas Valanciunas the Raptors jumped out to a 3-2 series lead and had Game Six well in hand when Kyle Lowry severely sprained his ankle on a drive to the bucket near the end of the third quarter. The Raptors seemed to fall apart after Lowry's injury and the Nets pulled out Game Six 100-94 and then won a grueling seventh game in Brooklyn when Joe Johnson hit a 16' runner at the buzzer, giving the Nets a narrow 94-93 victory.

The second round of the playoffs featured four great matchups including your Lakers facing off against division rival Golden State. The series started great as your Lakers breezed to an easy 108-89 victory in Game One. However, Game Two was much tougher as the Warriors team speed and long distance shooting helped them build an 85-69 lead going into the fourth quarter. Fueled by the manic defense of Rajon Rondo, excellent decision making of Kobe Bryant and lights out perimeter shooting of Kevin Love, your Lakers outscored the Warriors 33-16 in the final quarter and pulled out an amazing 102-101 come from behind victory behind Love's 34 points and 21 rebounds. The Warriors managed to win the third game by a score of 110-91 behind the hot shooting of the *Splash Brothers* but fell at home in Game Four 107-103. Your Lakers then closed them out in Game Five with a wire to wire 111-89 victory and a 4-1 series win.

The second seed Houston Rockets and MVP candidate James Harden squared off with Harden's old running mates Kevin Durant, Russell Westbrook and the Oklahoma City Thunder. Both Durant and Westbrook played fantastic all series long while Harden played efficient offensive basketball shooting over 50% from the floor and averaging over 27 points per game. However, it was ex-Laker Dwight Howard and his 24 point and 18 rebound series averages that devastated the Thunder, leading the Rockets to a 4-2 series victory.

In the Eastern Conference the top seed Cleveland Cavaliers made quick work of the Brooklyn Nets sweeping them in four straight games behind LeBron James second straight series averaging a triple double and the offensive wizardry of Kyrie Irving. James averaged 25.5 points, 10.5 rebounds and 10.5 assists while Irving torched Deron Williams, averaging 29.5 points per game. Kevin Garnett announced his retirement after the fourth and final game of the series and shocked everyone by stating, *I've reached an agreement in principle to buy the Minnesota Timberwolves and plan to rename them the Frozen Sota Garnett's and erect no less than 12 bronze statues of myself out front, one for each season I played in Minny. When asked why he would do such a thing, Garnett replied by saying, What else am I going to do with all the money I made, buy 100 homes in Los Angeles or 100,000 homes in Detroit? Nah, I want to own my own team!*

The second seed Indiana Pacers and third seed Chicago Bulls engaged in a marathon seven game series, complete with a total of seven overtime periods played. In the seventh and deciding game Paul George and Derrick Rose went mano-a-mano with the lightning quick Bulls point guard dropping 47 points on a barrage of layups and mid-range jumpers while the lanky Pacers wing scored 48 points thanks in large part to the 9 triples he drained. The one extra point Paul George scored turned out to be the difference in the game as the Pacers eliminated the Bulls in Game Seven 98-97 after Taj Gibson missed a wide open 12' jumper along the right baseline at the buzzer.

During the second round of the Playoffs the league announced its individual award winners, which were as follows:

Most Valuable Player:	LeBron James (Cavs)
Defensive Player of the Year:	LeBron James (Cavs)
Sixth Man of the Year:	Tyreke Evans (Pelicans)
Most Improved Player:	Anthony Bennett (Cavs)
Comeback P.O.Y.:	Kobe Bryant (Lakers)
Rookie of the Year:	Andrew Wiggins (Bucks)
Coach of the Year:	John Calipari (Cavs)

Your Lakers were well represented in the various award races with Kobe Bryant winning the *Comeback Player of the Year* award and Coach Jeff Van Gundy finishing second in the *Coach of the Year* award. Bryant also finished fourth in the MVP race, behind only LeBron James, Kevin Durant and Paul George while Kevin Love finished fifth in the *MVP* race. Rajon Rondo finished tenth in the *MVP* race as well as third in the *Comeback Player of the Year* voting behind only Bryant and the Bulls Derrick Rose. However, your Lakers were built to win the *Larry O'Brien Championship Trophy* and not merely individual awards.

The Conference Finals are now up for grabs and each Conference's top two seeds will be playing for the right to battle in the NBA Finals:

Your Lakers squared off with Dwight Howard's Houston Rockets. It was obvious from the start of the series that while Kobe Bryant was hell bent on destroying his former teammate and more importantly advancing to his eighth NBA Finals, the center known as *Superman* was extremely nervous, even terrified of failing on the biggest stage he'd been on since the 2009 NBA Finals when Bryant and the Lakers destroyed his Orlando Magic in just 5 games.

Western Conference Finals Game One: Game One was a massacre. With boos of *Dwi-ight Cow-ward* raining down each and every time the petulant center touched the ball, he played one of the worst games of his career going 0-7 from the floor and just 4-15 from the free throw line for a total of four points along with just 7 rebounds and a whopping 10 turnovers before fouling out early in the fourth quarter. Kobe Bryant on the other hand was masterful, playing one of the best games of his 19 year career. The man known as *Vino* shot 15-24 from the field including a remarkable 6-7 from distance and 15-15 from the free throw line for a total of 51 points to go along with 4 rebounds, 4 assists, 2 steals, 1 block and zero turnovers in just 32 minutes of game-time. Your Lakers won Game One 112-77.

Western Conference Finals Game Two: Game Two started much the same way as Game One, with Dwight Howard playing uninspired basketball and Bryant playing like a man touched by God Himself. However, unlike in Game One, Rajon Rondo got in early foul trouble and later was ejected in the third quarter after shoving and then elbowing Patrick Beverley, and Bryant played more of a facilitator role in Game Two with Coach Van Gundy being content to slow the game down considerably and let Bryant operate as the primary passer in half-court sets. Bryant ended up attempting just 13 shots in the game, making seven including one three-pointer along with hitting all 10 of his free-throw attempts. However, Bryant consistently found Pau Gasol for easy layups, connected on no less than three alley-oop dunks with Trevor Ariza and hit Kevin Love with a myriad of passes that led to multiple wide-open three pointers swishing through the net. When the final buzzer sounded your Lakers had won 101-89 with Bryant pouring in 25 points to go along with 16 assists, 6 rebounds, 4 steals, 2 blocks and just 2 turnovers in 38 minutes of action.

Western Conference Finals Game Three: Game Three was in Houston and Dwight Howard seemed ready to play from the start. After winning the opening tip, James Harden quickly found him for an alley-oop slam that seemed to get the big man going as he shot 5-6 in the first quarter en route to scoring 13 of the Rockets 31 first quarter points. Your Lakers scored just 13 first quarter points with Bryant and Love each held scoreless. However, Coach Van Gundy employed the *Hack-a-Howard* strategy for the rest of the game which frustrated the big man and proved to be Superman's kryptonite as he made just 6 of 17 free-throws the rest of the way, never scored another bucket and finished with just 19 points total.

Your Lakers outscored the Rockets 90-75 after the first quarter ended but with just 52 seconds left in the game were still behind 106-103. After a full timeout by Coach Van Gundy your Lakers ran a post play for Bryant, who with just one second left on the shot-clock buried a fade away jumper over a hand-in-the-face from Chandler Parsons making it 106-105 Rockets with just 29 seconds remaining in the game.

During the Rockets ensuing timeout Coach Van Gundy inserted Emeka Okafor and Metta World Peace into the game and removed Pau Gasol and Kevin Love. With Jeremy Lin locked down by Rajon Rondo, Chandler Parsons blanketed by Kobe Bryant, James Harden swamped by Trevor Ariza and Dwight Howard double covered by Emeka Okafor and Metta World Peace the Rockets went to Terrence Jones for a bucket. However as soon as Harden passed the ball to Jones, World Peace switched off Dwight Howard and hounded Jones into an off-balance, ugly jumper attempt that clanged off the rim into the waiting hands of Trevor Ariza.

After Ariza's rebound Coach Van Gundy called a full timeout, re-inserted Kevin Love and Pau Gasol into the game for Metta World Peace and Emeka Okafor and drew up an isolation play for Bryant to take a jump shot from the top of the key. Ariza then inbounded the ball to Bryant, who after a wicked pump fake that sent James Harden flying through the air to block a shot that would never come, found Pau Gasol for an alley-oop layup after Dwight Howard had left the paint thinking he could swat Bryant's shot. Gasol's lay-up was the final basket of the game and your Lakers escaped with a 107-106 victory and a 3-0 lead in the series.

Western Conference Finals Game Four: Game Four was a laugher. It looked as if the Rockets entire roster, coaching staff and ball boys knew the team had no chance of coming back and winning four straight games, and therefore decided to just mentally check out. Your Lakers cruised to an easy 108-91 victory and a sweep of the Rockets.

Kobe Bryant finished the series averaging 31.0 points, 7.0 assists and 4.5 rebounds per game, all while hitting on just over 60 percent of his field goal attempts in one of the most efficient series performances of his entire career. Dwight Howard on the other hand finished the series averaging just 13.0 points, 8.5 rebounds, .5 assists, 1.0 block and a whopping 6.5 turnovers per game while shooting an abysmal .375 from the field and .340 from the free-throw line.

In the Eastern Conference Finals the top seed Cleveland Cavaliers faced off against the Indiana Pacers. The dynamic duo of LeBron James and Kyrie Irving were more than up for the challenge Indiana's great team defense would present. Irving did his part by leading both teams in scoring, averaging 26.5 points per game while also dishing 6.5 dimes per game while James dominated the entire series and even counterpart Paul George by once again averaging a triple double with 22.5 points, 10.0 rebounds and 11.5 assists per game in leading the Cavaliers to an unexpected sweep of the Pacers.

It appeared that *King James* was on a mission like never before, a mission to not only destroy the one active player (Kobe Bryant) pundits felt he needed to eclipse in career achievements to ascend the list of all-time greats, but to also cement himself on his own personal NBA Mount Rushmore. James took flak from many talking heads and even from the great Bill Russell when he left the 11-time NBA champion off his personal Mount Rushmore list during a 2014 interview, a list that featured Michael Jordan, Magic Johnson, Larry

Bird and Oscar Robertson. However various hoops fans, possibly including James himself, do not consider Bill Russell as one of the four greatest players of all-time as they do not consider *team* success as one of the most important factors when comparing individual players and judging such players individual excellence. For example, in the minds of many fans Wilt Chamberlain was simply a better basketball player and far more dominant than Bill Russell and therefore to rank Chamberlain below Russell on a fictional NBA Mount Rushmore simply because he wasn't surrounded by the same great players Russell was is insane. Regardless, LeBron James was on his own personal quest to surpass Kobe Bryant as well as Larry Bird and Oscar Robertson and to firmly set himself on his own personal NBA Mount Rushmore alongside Michael Jordan and Magic Johnson, and whoever else anyone wants to throw up their as the fourth all-time great.

This year's NBA Finals were the most watched in history. Fans around the world had been waiting years to see Kobe Bryant square off against LeBron James in a championship series. They finally got what they had been waiting for.

The Cavaliers entered the NBA Finals as the prohibitive favorites after posting a 71-11 regular season record and perfect 12-0 record throughout the Eastern Conference Playoffs. They held a publicly unspoken belief that if they could beat your Lakers in the Finals in 5 games or less they would become the greatest team in the history of the NBA. The Michael Jordan, Scottie Pippen and Dennis Rodman led 1995-96 Chicago Bulls had finished with a better regular season record than these Cavaliers, but they also lost three playoff games that season, including two NBA Finals games. The 95-96 Bulls final record was 87 wins and 13 losses. If the Cavaliers could beat your Lakers in 5 games or less they would match the Bulls 87 wins but would have less than 13 losses and thereby a better total win percentage than that great 95-96 Bulls team.

Your Lakers entered the NBA Finals coming off an utter dismantling and unexpected sweep of Dwight Howard and the Houston Rockets. They had finished 67-15 on the season and had rolled through the Western Conference playoffs posting a 12-1 record as well. With the Cavaliers recording an 83-11 record and your Lakers a 79-16 record this Finals would boast the highest total winning percentage of the two Conference Champions in league history! When the Chicago Bulls and Seattle Supersonics met in the 1996 NBA Finals the Bulls had a 83-11 record and the Sonics had a 75-22 record for a combined total winning percentage of .827; your Lakers and this year's Cavaliers have a combined total winning percentage of .857!

Before the series started LeBron James was asked what beating the Lakers and especially Kobe Bryant in a championship series would mean for his legacy. He replied, *I mean, I just want another ring, that's it. It's not about beating Kobe, I just want to add to my ring count. No doubt Kobe is one of the greatest players ever but I just want another title and I don't care who I have to go through to get it.*

When told of James' comments by Magic Johnson during a pre-Finals interview, Bryant responded, *LeBron's great, maybe the greatest small forward to ever play but he gave you a political answer. He wants to beat me bad, you can count on that. I've got five rings and he doesn't and if I tie Jordan by beating him that will kill him. It will mess with his head and mess with his legacy. He can't let me, especially this 36 year old version of me, beat him when he has home-court advantage, he just can't. If I get my sixth ring in this series, he has no shot of ever eclipsing me on an All-Time Greatest list, let alone Jordan. LeBron knows that and I expect him to play great but I expect to have my sixth ring when this series is over too, you better believe that.*

Magic Johnson started laughing his famous laugh and said, Kobe, *I know you've got that old man mentality now, like you can just say whatever you want, but you may not want to poke the bear, you know what I mean?* Kobe smirked and said, Magic, *you know me man. I just don't care. I am an old dog now and I don't care what anyone thinks about me except my wife, my family and God. I'm just speaking the truth. I know LeBron will hear about this, I just don't care. That ring is mine. I'm like Frodo and he's like Gollum and I'm coming for my precious.*

Magic almost doubled-over from laughter before saying, *And what about Michael. You mentioned MJ. If you do win this ring, where do you think you personally stack up on the list of All-Time Greats? Will you be ready to retire?* Kobe shakes his head and chuckles before saying, Really? *You're going to ask me about retiring if I win my sixth ring? Come on Magic, you know me better than that. If I win number six this year you better believe I will want number seven even more. Once I get seven then you can ask me about retirement but honestly I'm not even thinking about that right now. As for Jordan, Mike knows he's sitting on the throne right now. He knows he's number one with a bullet, but yeah if I get number six this year, I think I'm right there with him. I'm going to retire with more career regular season and playoff points, assists, rebounds and wins than MJ and if I match his ring count I think I'll be right there at the top with him … until I get number seven.*

The Finals for the Ages was set and it seemed no one could get enough news, coverage, gossip and predictions. Magic Johnson believed the Lakers would shock the world and win the series in just 6 games. Larry Bird felt LeBron James would lead the Cavaliers to a tough seven game victory. Michael Jordan himself simply said he wouldn't bet against Kobe even though he thought the Cavaliers should be the odds-on favorites. Most talking heads however seemed to agree with the Vegas odds-makers prediction that the Cavaliers would win the series in just 5 games. However, as Buster Douglas and Mike Tyson know, Vegas isn't always right.

NBA Finals Game One: Game One resembled a heavyweight boxing match with both teams seemingly feeling each other out and taking it slow in the first quarter and four minutes or so of the second. When most of the starters checked back in for both sides with about 8 minutes to go in the first half, the teams were deadlocked 33-33. However, in the last 8 minutes of the first half Kevin Love caught fire; the player some consider the 21st century version of Larry Bird (or at least a better rebounding version of Dirk Nowitzki) scored 13 points in the last 8 minutes of the half and your Lakers went into the locker room with a 51-48 lead.

The third quarter was more of the same; neither team pulled ahead and each team's superstars (Bryant and Love as well as James and Irving) shouldered the load offensively. The third quarter ended with your Lakers up 76-75.

The first four minutes of the fourth quarter were disastrous for your Lakers. With both Kobe Bryant and Kevin Love on the bench and LeBron James and Kyrie Irving staying on the court the Cavs out-scored your Lakers 10-4; when Bryant and Love checked back into the game your Lakers were behind 85-80 with just 8 minutes to play.

Over the next 8 minutes LeBron James played the role of facilitator with teammate Kyrie Irving being the prime benefactor, while your

Lakers relied on Kobe Bryant to bail them out time and time again with the shot clock running down after the Cavaliers had stifled their attempts at quick buckets. With just 58 seconds left in the game and the Cavaliers ahead 97-95 LeBron James held the ball at the top of the key. He feigned left and then took a couple of dribbles to the right before shooting a fall away jumper over Trevor Ariza that clanged off the right side of the rim and into the hands of Kevin Love. Love quickly flipped the ball to Rajon Rondo who took no more than two dribbles before zipping a beautiful cross-court bounce pass to Kobe Bryant for a wide-open three pointer that swished through the net giving your Lakers a 98-97 lead with 28 seconds remaining.

After Cavaliers Coach John Calipari's timeout, LeBron James inbounded the ball to Kyrie Irving who dribbled the shot clock down to 4 seconds before making his move to the basket. Irving got into the lane with ease, split two defenders and made a nice floater from 8 feet over Pau Gasol to give the Cavaliers a one point lead with just five seconds left in the game.

After Coach Van Gundy drew up the final play during a 20 second timeout Trevor Ariza inbounded the ball to Kobe Bryant who had LeBron James draped all over him. Bryant gave a quick pump fake, spun to his left, took two dribbles and started to rise for a fall-away jumper from 20'. However before releasing the shot, Bryant noticed Kyrie Irving flying at him from the left and leaving Rajon Rondo all alone just inside the three-point line. Bryant gave a flick of his left wrist and passed the ball to a wide open Rondo who let fly, burying the shot and giving your Lakers a 100-99 victory and a 1-0 lead in the series.

NBA Finals Game Two: The Cleveland Cavaliers looked like an entirely different team in Game Two. Gone were the jitters and cautious play they displayed in the first game. LeBron and company were ready for a no-holds-barred street-fight this time around.

The Cavs quickly jumped on your Lakers, outscoring them 11-0 in the game's first 3 minutes en route to building a 35-19 lead at the end of the first quarter. The second quarter was better for your Lakers, though not by much, as they were outscored 27-20 and entered halftime down 62-39.

Kobe Bryant, who had only shot the ball three times in the first half, missing all three attempts and scoring just 5 points on free throws, came out firing in the third quarter. The *Black Mamba* attempted to rekindle some of that first game magic in which he poured in 30 points to lead all scorers. However, while Bryant scored a solid 14 points in the third quarter he needed 12 shots to do so and your Lakers entered the fourth quarter down 85-68.

Bryant stayed on the floor for the entire fourth quarter and continued his high-volume scoring act, adding 13 points on 11 shots. Bryant finished with 32 points on 26 shots while LeBron James managed to score 30 points on just 14 shots, thanks in large part to making 12 of 14 free-throws. Game Two went to the Cavaliers 106-97.

NBA Finals Game Three: Back in Los Angeles the Lakers were actually expected to win Game Three and take a 2-1 series lead; however it was the Cleveland Cavaliers who looked like the home team, played with poise and took it to your Lakers from the opening tip. The entire game was one big stinker from start to finish for L.A. as LeBron James did his normal *King James* thing and recorded a triple double with 25 points, 11 rebounds and 10 assists while Kyrie Irving erupted for a game-leading 31 points on just 17 shots, thanks to the six three-pointers he drained. Even reserve Anthony Bennett actually played like a former #1 pick and outscored Kobe Bryant 20-19.

When Anthony Bennett outscores Kobe Bryant, you can't expect to win many games. Game Three was no exception as the Cavs entirely annihilated your Lakers 109-78.

NBA Finals Game Four: The atmosphere was tense to start Game Four, not merely NBA Finals tense but one-and-done elimination tense, best friends fighting over a girl tense. Just 30 seconds into the game LeBron James dunked on Kevin Love and finished the highlight-reel play with a shove and scream. Less than two minutes later Kobe Bryant delivered a hard foul on Kyrie Irving that left the star point guard bleeding from the right eye-brow.

By the time the first quarter buzzer sounded the teams had combined for twenty personal fouls, four technical fouls and just 38 points with the game tied 19-19. Pau Gasol was the Lakers leading scorer with 7 points while Dion Waiters was the Cavs leading scorer with 6 points.

The second quarter was played at a feverish pace and while just as heated as the first, the teams actually seemed capable of playing defense without trying to bludgeon or decapitate each other. At half-time the teams were knotted 43-43 and though it was still anyone's game one had the feeling that this was the Lakers game to lose, more than the Cavs game to win. LeBron and Kyrie each had three fouls and Kyrie could not find his shooting touch, hitting just 2-11 shots and scoring a total of 4 points.

The third quarter seemed to resemble the first in many ways, not the least of which was the *Inquisition* like bloodshed and maniacal tempers. Jordan Farmar and Metta World Peace were each ejected near the end of the third quarter with both throwing punches. Farmar took a wild swing at Kyrie Irving who had shoved him from behind on a layup attempt while World Peace connected on a straight jab to the jaw of Tyler Zeller who had first swung on him in the melee. The third quarter ended with the teams deadlocked at 77-77.

The fourth quarter started with a bang as Jodie Meeks picked Jarett Jack's pocket and fed Xavier Henry for a thunderous slam over Cavs backup point guard Matthew Dellavedova. Your Lakers held a solid 6 point lead with just 5 minutes to play before Dion Waiters, who had been on fire all game, went on another scoring barrage. Waiters dropped 11 points over the next 4:30 of game time and tied the game up at 101 on a deep three-pointer drilled right in the face of Kobe Bryant.

The final 30 seconds of game time seemed to last an entire quarter though there would be just two possessions. Kyrie Irving held the ball at the top of the key with the clock ticking down; Cavs Coach John Calipari had called for Dion Waiters to come off a screen and then to either take an open jumper along the left baseline or fire a quick pass back out to Irving or James if covered. The play actually worked exactly the way the Cavs wanted it too with Waiters coming off a Joel Embiid screen and catching a pass along the left baseline and Kobe Bryant a solid 6 feet away. However, as soon as Waiters caught the ball Trevor Ariza left LeBron James and closed out on Waiters faster than *Twista* spits lyrics; Ariza got just enough of the shot to make it fall a few feet short of the basket and into the waiting arms of Kevin Love who was always in the right place at the right time throughout the game.

After Kobe Bryant called timeout with 11 seconds remaining in the game Coach Van Gundy called for a simple isolation play, choosing to place the ball in Rajon Rondo's capable hands and let him make the final decision of who shoots and from where. When Rondo got the ball he held it for a few seconds before making his move toward the right baseline. When he got to the baseline and it appeared he was going to go all the way to the rack and try to win the game himself, he quickly spun back towards the middle of court, took one dribble towards the free-throw line and jumped. Joel Embiid was sure Rondo was shooting for the win, left his man and jumped out to block the shot just as Rondo threw a perfect, soft lob-pass toward the right side of the rim ... and into the hands of Kevin Love who caught the alley-oop and slammed it through the net as time expired. Your Lakers won Game Four 103-101 to tie the series at 2-2.

NBA Finals Game Five: The teams returned to Cleveland tied at two games apiece and with both Metta World Peace and Jordan Farmar of the Lakers, as well as Tyler Zeller of the Cavs, suspended due to their respective roles in the Game Four melee. Game Five would be more akin to a massacre than a melee as other than Kobe Bryant and Kevin Love the Lakers players didn't even bother to show up.

Bryant and Love poured in 30 points apiece; however their teammates combined to score just 29 points. The Cavaliers on the other hand had seven players in double figures, led by LeBron James with 24 points, and scoured an astounding 122 points to drub your Lakers by 33 points, 122-89.

NBA Finals Game Six: Back in Los Angeles for Game Six your Lakers found themselves in their first win-or-go-home game of the year. They responded like true champions do.

While the usual suspects all came to play, it was Rajon Rondo that stood out amongst the crowd and was the best player on the floor in Game Six. Rondo controlled the game from the opening tip and by the time the third quarter ended he had already registered a triple double with 17 points, 12 assists and 12 rebounds to go along with 3 steals and a block. Perhaps most importantly, Rondo hadn't turned the ball over even one time.

Your Lakers entered the fourth quarter with a 84-76 lead and the game seemingly in control ... then Kyrie Irving caught fire. Irving buried five three-pointers and scored 19 points to lead the Cavaliers to an improbable 106-102 lead with just 39 seconds remaining in the game. After yet another layup by Rajon Rondo, followed by a missed three-pointer by Kyrie Irving that would have iced the game for the Cavaliers but was an ill-advised shot attempt, your Lakers found themselves down 106-104 with just 17 seconds remaining.

After a full timeout by Coach Van Gundy the Lakers took the floor and Trevor Ariza calmly inbounded the ball to Rajon Rondo for what looked to be a typical isolation play. Rondo had been magnificent the entire game, passing like a wizard and rebounding like a warrior as usual, but also being able to score almost at will on the poor defense of Kyrie Irving to the tune of 20 points on just 11 shot attempts.

After receiving the inbounds pass Rondo and Kobe Bryant played hot potato a couple times before Rondo held the ball for 2-3 seconds to let the clock run down to just 8 seconds; when the clock hit 8 Rondo attacked. The diminutive point guard with the insane wing span blew by Kyrie Irving on his way to the basket; however as he made his way into the paint he realized he could either attempt an extremely difficult floater over Joel Embiid or use his body as a shield and try to draw a foul with little hope of making the layup attempt.

Rondo chose to try and draw a foul but while he was taking his final dribble towards the basket Kevin Love was quickly yet quietly drifting to the three-point line and away from the defense of Tristan Thompson. Rondo spotted a wide-open Love out of the corner of his eye and fired a perfect pass just a split-second before he was about to leap and undoubtedly crash into Embiid. Love caught Rondo's perfect pass with just 4 seconds on the clock, feigned a quick pass to Kobe Bryant to freeze the defense ... and then let fly. The ball swished through the net as the buzzer sounded and Love's arms raised triumphantly for all to see.

Your Lakers won the series penultimate game 107-106 due in large part to the all-around dominance of Rajon Rondo who finished with 20 points, 15 assists and 16 rebounds. The series was knotted at 3 games apiece and headed back to Quicken Loans Arena in Cleveland for a decisive Game Seven.

Going into Game Seven, most talking heads felt the series would end with LeBron James holding both the *Larry O'Brien Championship Trophy* as well as the *Bill Russell NBA Finals Most Valuable Player Award*. James had averaged a triple-double with 26.5 points, 10.5 rebounds and 10.0 assists per game and while Lakers stars Kobe Bryant (25.5 points, 4.5 rebounds and 4.0 assists), Kevin Love (23.0 points and 14.5 rebounds) and Rajon Rondo (12.5 points, 12.0

assists and 7.5 rebounds) had all played magnificent basketball, it was the man known as *King James* who had given the most virtuoso performances on a consistent basis.

Though the series was knotted at 3 games apiece the Cavaliers had outscored your Lakers 644-573, or by an average of 11.8 points per game through the first 6 games of the series, and the consensus in Vegas was that the Cavs would win Game Seven by at least 12 points. Even Magic Johnson himself stated, *I'm afraid that unless Kobe can drop 50 and LeBron James becomes passive to a fault the Cavs are going to win this title.*

NBA Finals Game Seven: When Game Seven began the Lakers starting five of Rajon Rondo, Kobe Bryant, Trevor Ariza, Kevin Love and Pau Gasol refused to acknowledge their Cleveland Cavaliers counterparts whatsoever, which made for an awkward scene and seemed to catch the Cavaliers off-guard. LeBron James seemed especially miffed when after he offered his hand to Kobe, the five-time champion waved him off with a disgusted snort and a rather homicidal glare.

After winning the opening tip the Lakers scored a quick bucket on a beautiful bounce pass from Rondo to Gasol who flushed the ball through the hoop with unusual force, and then in an extremely uncharacteristic move, the big Spaniard let out a scream and stared down Joel Embiid who had tried to block the dunk. Referee Monty McCutchen slapped Gasol with a technical foul and after Kyrie Irving sunk the freebie the lines had been drawn and the battle was on.

The first quarter was an exercise in frantic aggression and offensive inefficiency and hearkened back to Game 7 of the 2010 NBA Finals between the Lakers and Celtics. However, unlike that Game 7, your Lakers didn't find themselves in a 9 point hole at the end of the first 12 minutes but rather a 21-21 tie.

The second quarter was more of the same with each team's defense being more solid than its offense, though the Cavaliers offense did seem to be humming at a better clip than the Lakers. There were even two plays that left the crowd in hysterics. The first was an amazing half-court alley-oop from Kyrie Irving to LeBron James which James caught with his back to the basket and proceeded to bring the ball down to his knees before hammering it home in a move more suited to NBA 2K than a real NBA game. The second was a tip-dunk executed by Anthony Bennett. Dion Waiters had just taken a long jumper from the right baseline and as the ball caromed off the rim, into what seemed to be the waiting hands of Pau Gasol, Bennett came flying through the air from the left baseline, caught the ball with his right hand, quickly grabbed it with his left hand as well and then seemed to climb up the back of Gasol before slamming the ball with a remarkable amount of force, so much in fact that the crowd seemed almost shocked that the backboard didn't shatter.

When the second quarter buzzer sounded, the Cavaliers held a 46-42 lead, though both teams entered their respective locker rooms knowing this was anyone's game. The leading scorer, rebounder, dime-dropper, stealer and blocker for the Cavaliers was LeBron James, who despite turning the ball over four times already and missing all three of his three-point attempts had managed to score 13 points, pull down 7 rebounds, dish out 5 assists, swipe three passes and block 2 shots including one Kevin Love dunk attempt. The Lakers attack was more varied with Pau Gasol leading the team in scoring with 11 points, Kevin Love leading the team in rebounding with 10 boards, Rajon Rondo leading the team in assists with 6, Kobe Bryant leading the team in steals with 2 and Trevor Ariza leading the team in blocks with 2, including a come-from-behind block on a Kyrie Irving layup attempt at the end of the first half.

Back in the Lakers locker room Coach Van Gundy implored his team to continue playing tough defense, not to give an inch of breathing room to LeBron James or Kyrie Irving, and above all else, not to give up any easy layups. When backup point guard Jordan Farmar said, *Coach, the refs seem to be calling the game really close and making it hard to be all that aggressive. Van Gundy then lit into Farmar and the entire team saying, I don't care about the refs, you let me and Stan deal with the refs. All I care about is you making life miserable on the Cavs. I don't want to see them get even one easy layup in the second half, not one. If you're a backup, like you are Jordan, I'd rather see you guys get ejected after blowing up a Cav who thinks he's going to get an easy layup than just watch the ball drop through the hoop trying to avoid the foul. You guys know I coached the nasty Knicks, you know my teams were known for their pluckiness and defensive dominance. You know I threw myself at Alonzo Mourning during that melee back in the 98' playoffs; and who won that series? My Knicks did! Alonzo was freaked out the rest of that series; he knew if I had to I would grab that ankle again but this time I would chew it right off his leg! Now go out there and chew off LeBron's leg if you have to, just win this game! Assistant Coach Chuck Person stood up and said, Yeah, what Jeff said, chew off their legs if you have to, just win this game!*

Your Lakers took the court in the third quarter ready for *Armageddon*. Just four minutes into the third and it was obvious Jordan Farmar took Coach Van Gundy's words to heart as much as a Biblical Christian takes the words of Christ to heart. Dion Waiters had beat Kobe Bryant on a back-door cut and was gliding in for an easy uncontested layup when Farmar came crashing into him.

When the two tumbled to the floor Waiters gave Farmar and elbow and Farmar responded with one of his own. The two players continued to tussle before being separated by the referees and ultimately thrown out of the game for striking each other. Needless to say, the loss of star shooting guard Waiters was a far greater blow to the Cavaliers than was the loss of backup point guard Farmar to your Lakers. Los Angeles took advantage of Waiters' ejection and outscored the Cavaliers 27-23 in the third quarter, tying the game at 69 apiece heading into the final quarter of the final game of the 2014-15 season.

While both Coach Calipari and Coach Van Gundy usually started fourth quarters with their starters getting some much needed rest on the bench, each coach decided to let their starters play the entire fourth quarter in this do-or-die game. The only exception was Cleveland's Dion Waiters who was replaced by Jarrett Jack after his ejection.

The fourth quarter was filled with fireworks, both on the court and on the sidelines. While each team rose to the challenge and competed at a high level, each team had a coach that seemed to wilt under the pressure. Cavaliers Coach John Calipari was hit with a technical foul half way through the fourth quarter after vehemently objecting to a charging call on LeBron James and just two minutes later Lakers Assistant Coach Chuck Person was slapped with two technicals and thrown out of the game after storming the court and berating referee Joey Crawford for calling a technical on Trevor Ariza, for what appeared to be nothing more than a harmless facial expression given after Crawford called him for goaltending on a Kyrie Irving layup attempt.

With just four minutes remaining in the game the Cavaliers held a 93-90 lead thanks in large part to Kyrie Irving's nine fourth quarter points. Over the next 3:15 of game time the Lakers and Cavaliers each scored six points with Kyrie Irving hitting two more three-point-ers (giving him 15 points in the fourth quarter and 30 points for the game) and Kobe Bryant nailing one three-pointer and converting one incredibly difficult three point play (giving him a team-leading 29 points for the game).

After a quick steal by Rajon Rondo off an inbounds pass, and yet another layup by Kevin Love cut the Cavaliers lead to 99-98 with 29 seconds remaining, Cavs Coach John Calipari called a timeout to set up the play he hoped would win him his first title. On the Lakers sideline Coach Van Gundy held the team's full attention. He told the team he was positive, absolutely positive that the Cavaliers were going to use LeBron James as a decoy and distributor on their final play and that they were going to the on-fire Kyrie Irving for their final shot.

Coach Van Gundy took Kevin Love and Pau Gasol out of the game, inserted Metta World Peace and Emeka Okafor and also instructed Trevor Ariza to guard LeBron James but to give him a solid cushion as he was sure James would not take a jumper, even a wide-open jumper, in this situation. He also instructed Kobe Bryant to guard Kyrie Irving and to body him up and for Rajon Rondo to guard Jarrett Jack but to immediately double Irving the second he catches the ball, even if that meant leaving Jack wide open. Emeka Okafor was assigned to Tristan Thompson and Metta World Peace was assigned to Anthony Bennett with instructions to box out like crazy.

Just as Coach Van Gundy thought, the Cavaliers inbounded the ball to LeBron James at the top of the key for what looked to be an isolation play. James held the ball until there was just 10 seconds left on the shot clock before making his move towards the basket. James dribbled to his right, tucked his head and started a foray into the line. Trevor Ariza was draped on James like a blanket however and before James got into the paint, he stopped, gave one quick pump fake and then fired a pass to the right baseline for Kyrie Irving who had just come off a screen set by Tristan Thompson and broken free from the defense of Kobe Bryant.

By the time Kyrie caught James' pass and turned to face the basket Bryant had recovered and was in position to challenge the shot. Rajon Rondo had also left Dion Waiters just as Coach Van Gundy had instructed him to do and was sneakily making his way towards Irving as well.

Irving then gave a dribble towards the right baseline before executing a lightning fast spin back towards the middle of the court, followed by one more dribble to his left and then elevating to shoot a fade-away jump-shot. However, just as the ball left his finger-tips, Rondo's outstretched hand swatted the ball out of bounds, but before the ball landed Metta World Peace leapt and batted the ball back inbounds to Emeka Okafor who quickly called time out with just 9 seconds remaining in the game and your Lakers trailing 99-98.

During the timeout, Coach Van Gundy gathered his troops and simply said, *Give the ball to Kobe and get out of the way; and Kobe, make the right play.* Kobe Bryant responded by saying, *Don't worry Jeff, I got this. Kevin, float to the three-point line; Rajon and Trevor, crash the boards; Pau, let's play some pick and roll big fella.*

When your Lakers took the floor they noticed Kyrie Irving was nowhere to be found. LeBron James was guarding Kobe, Jarrett Jack was guarding Rondo, Tristan Thompson was guarding Trevor Ariza, Joel Embiid was guarding Kevin Love and Tyler Zeller was guarding Pau Gasol. No matter, Kobe was getting the ball.

As soon as Kobe Bryant caught Trevor Ariza's inbound pass, LeBron James was in his face. Bryant calmly held the ball for two seconds, time enough for Pau Gasol to set a screen just inside the three-point line at the center of the court. Bryant rolled to his right and used Gasol's pick to get into the lane. As he reached the right side of the lane, Joel Embiid left Kevin Love to come double Bryant. Bryant then spun quickly to his left, splitting the LeBron James and Embiid double-team, took one more dribble towards the rim, gave a quick head-fake and began to spin once again to attempt a fade away jumper from just inside the free-throw line.

However, just before Bryant was about to elevate he saw Tyler Zeller leave Pau Gasol and charge towards him, obviously with the intention of blocking his jump-shot. Bryant waited a split second, did a 180' spin ... and then ... just as Zeller leaped towards him, threaded a beautiful bounce pass between and under the legs of Zeller to a wide-open Pau Gasol who let fly from 19'.

Gasol's shot swished through the net as time expired. Quicken Loans arena went dead-silent.

The Lakers bench emptied in celebration. Your Lakers, the team whose roster you built, the team whose coach you hired, the team whose trade's you executed, your Lakers won the NBA Championship!

NBA Commission Adam Silver presented Jeanie, Jim and the entire Buss family with the *Larry O'Brien Championship Trophy. Bill Russell* stood by the platform ready to present the *Bill Russell NBA Finals Most Valuable Player Award*.

Kobe Bryant finished the Finals averaging 26.0 points, 4.1 assists and 4.7 rebounds while shooting a magnificent .504 from the floor. Rajon Rondo finished the series averaging 12.0 points, 12.0 assists,

7.0 rebounds and 3.0 steals. Kevin Love averaged 23.6 points, 13.6 rebounds and 3.1 assists per game during the series. All three players were worthy of winning Finals MVP.

Commissioner Silver motioned for the great Bill Russell to make his way to the stage while saying, *In the history of the NBA Finals there has never been Co-MVP's … until now. I'm pleased to present this award to Co-MVP's Kobe Bryant of the Los Angeles Laker and LeBron James of the Cleveland Cavaliers. LeBron James becomes just the second player from a losing team in league history to win this award while Kobe Bryant wins this award for the third time in his storied career. Each superstar played magnificent basketball throughout this epic series.*

LeBron James was not only the leading scorer in this series averaging 26.1 points but also became the first player in Finals history to average a triple-double, contributing 11.0 rebounds and 10.1 assists as well. Kobe Bryant led his team in scoring at 26.0 points per game and saved his best performance for last in this remarkable Game Seven we just had. Congratulations to both 6-time champion Kobe Bryant and LeBron James, two deserving NBA Finals Most Valuable Players!

EXIT MEETING WITH JIM BUSS

Lakers Owner Jim Buss: *You did it baby, you did it! You took over the worst team the Lakers had ever had since moving to Los Angles 54 years ago and turned it into an NBA champion in one year!*

You have proven yourself to be a veritable basketball genius, a General Manager mastermind! I always knew I hired the right person for this job. There were a couple times where I questioned you but I never lost faith that you would get the job done, and that's exactly what you did!

You're an NBA champion and I want you to know that if you want to be here, I want you here. I know there are a lot of teams out there that will offer you the moon to come and rescue their team and take over as GM, but those teams aren't the Los Angeles Lakers, your Los Angeles Lakers!

All I can say is congratulations and I hope you will sign a long-term extension with us. Great job champ!

EPILOGUE

Writing this book (as well as *Saving the Celtics: A Be the General manager Book*) has been a blast and I hope you enjoyed reading it as much as I enjoyed writing it. There aren't many sports fans on the planet that have been blessed with the ability to write such a book as this, the free time needed to complete such a project as this and the loving and understanding wife and children necessary to support one's dedication to such a work as this. I am a blessed man.

I know that not all fans will agree with the course one must follow in this book in order to win the NBA title. I imagine there are many readers who feel that Rajon Rondo and Kobe Bryant could never co-exist or that Kevin Love and Pau Gasol could never combine to play good enough defense to stifle such high-scoring and unstoppable frontcourt duos as Kendrick *I can't believe I haven't been amnestied yet* Perkins and Serge Ibaka. There may even be many readers out there who feel that a Carmelo Anthony and Kobe Bryant pairing would assure the Lakers an immediate championship, despite all reason and logic saying otherwise.

The point of this book is not to set forth the most perfect plan the Lakers should follow this summer, as in reality such may be building for the future and not trying to win a title immediately at all, for as any fan knows two titles in 10 years is better than one title immediately with none to follow in the next nine years. Rather, this book is merely meant as a fun exercise in armchair General Management and nothing more. However, I will say that if the goal is to win a title *this season*, the future be damned, than the plan this book outlines is perhaps better than any other floating around in the ether at this time, period.

It's fun to read articles about what could have been such as hindsight drafts. For example, it's fun to think about how Michael Jordan's and for that matter Clyde Drexler's careers would have played out had Jordan been drafted by the Portland Trailblazers instead of Sam Bowie. Would Jordan have scored far less career points and won less individual trophies but even more rings than he did in Chicago? Would Drexler have been willing to play Robin to Jordan's Batman or would chemistry issues have caused the team to go ring-less while the two players were on the same roster? What if Jordan would have been drafted #1 overall in the 1984 draft as he should have been and Hakeem Olajuwon been drafted second by the Portland Trailblazers to team with Drexler? Would Jordan be ring-less and Hakeem and Clyde sitting pretty on an NBA Mount Rushmore list with six rings apiece?

Thinking about what could have transpired if a team would or wouldn't have made a particular trade is also a fun mental exercise. For example, what would have happened had Kobe Bryant not used his no-trade-clause and vetoed the agreement Dr. Jerry Buss had to send the then 3-time champion to the Detroit Pistons for Rip Hamilton, Tayshaun Prince, Amir Johnson and a first round pick? Would the Lakers still be looking for their first post Kobe& Shaq title? Would Kobe have seven rings by now with four coming as a Piston thereby topping Michael Jordan's six titles and assuring that Kobe would one day enter the Hall of Fame as a Piston rather than a Laker?

The possibilities are almost endless when it comes to thinking about the what-could-have-been in sports and thinking about what could have been can be extremely fun. However, the fun one can have thinking about what could have been actually pales in comparison to the fun one can have thinking about what could be in the future, as such mere thoughts could still become reality.

Becoming a sports seer or basketball prophet would be an insanely enjoyable way to earn a living. Writing this book allowed me to become such for a time and it would be great to see this book spark an entirely new genre of sports fiction: *Be the General Manager.*

Readers of all ages have loved *Choose Your Own Adventure* books since the idea was first conceived by Princeton University and Columbia Law School graduate Edward Packard. Packard's first title was *Sugarcane Island* which was released in 1976 as an *Adventures of You* series published by Vermont Crossroads Press. Bantam Books started publishing the *Choose Your Own Adventure* series shortly thereafter selling more than 250,000,000 copies between 1979 (the year I was born) and 1998 (the year after I married my high school sweetheart and our first child was conceived).I think it's high time *Be the General Manager* books become every bit as popular!

APPENDIX ONE:
Initiating, or Avoiding, the Kobepacalypse

It's no secret that Kobe Bryant's desire was to remain a *Laker for life* and that he took great pride in only having played for one team his entire career at the time he signed his recent two year $48,500,000 extension. However, it's also no great mystery that Kobe Bryant doesn't seem to be willing to play for less than he's worth, which is one thing he may have learned from his old running mate and quasi-nemesis Shaquille O'Neal.

Ever since the day Bryant put pen to paper on the aforementioned two year $48,500,000 contract, Lakers fans have been divided. Some feel that Kobe should be commended for taking a pay-cut (he could have received a maximum amount of $66,349,473.75 over two years under the new *Collective Bargaining*

Agreement), while others feel he should be condemned for accepting more than he is now worth. Some fans feel the Lakers brass was wise to make Kobe happy, treat him like the franchise savior he was and financially reward him for past successes while others feel Lakers brass was remiss in their duties, put an individual ahead of the team, and that it would be great if the Buss family sold the Lakers to a group of real fans like Jack Nicholson, Penny Marshall, Dyan Cannon and Leonardo DiCaprio. The debates are heated and heavy and both sides have some strong points.

Personally, I can see both sides. I can understand why many die-hard Lakers fan are frustrated that Kobe Bryant didn't sign for the NBA minimum which would have allowed the Lakers to sign both LeBron James *and* Carmelo Anthony to maximum level contracts this summer, as all fans want are wins, wins and more wins. I can also understand why management offered and why Kobe accepted the two year $48,500,000 deal. Management may have been worried that had they low-balled Kobe he would have balked at such an insulting offer and chose rather to test the market in free agency this summer, while Kobe himself certainly thought he was worth the $48,500,000 and a great deal more for all he has done for the franchise in the past and because he was going to be giving his all to the franchise going forward.

Had I been the Lakers General Manager last season I too would have wanted to *lock up* Kobe with a long-term contract extension. However, there is absolutely no way I would have done so *before* seeing him play and being assured he could continue to perform at a high-level. I do not believe ownership's mistake was in offering Kobe the amount they did but simply making such an offer *before* they even had the chance to evaluate Kobe's on-court performance and have a solid understanding of what sort of payer he was going to be on the court going forward. Regardless, hindsight is 20-20 and I think it's quite obvious that Lakers brass did not foresee Kobe missing almost the entire 2013-14 season when they offered him the two year $48,500,000 contract.

Many Lakers fans are furious that close to 40 percent of this upcoming season's salary cap is dedicated to one player who will turn 36 years old during the season.

These fans actually seem to feel that the Kobepacalypse has descended upon them and that the Lakers will never win another title as long as Kobe Bryant is on the roster. However, there are other fans, myself included, that feel the real Kobepacalypse is what Lakers brass avoided by offering Bryant the contract they did. Allow me to explain.

Kobe is a very proud man and he is nothing if not intelligent. Bryant is not some knucklehead that skipped college because he couldn't qualify academically. He's very intelligent and he's a businessman as well. He hasn't squandered his earnings like many other sports stars before him and he's also very aware of his legacy and standing in the historical annals (or is it anals, eh Darrell Sheets?) of the game of basketball. Simply put, as Darrel Sheets would say, Kobe Bryant is an *upper chalant* (i.e upper echelon, but in *Sheetsnacular* a curious mixture of upper echelon and nonchalant) player with a very personalized sense of his own market worth.

Had Lakers brass offered Kobe any amount he felt was an insult (be it $10,000,000 or $20,000,000 as only Kobe knows what number he would have considered insulting) I honestly believe Bryant would have strongly and sincerely considered signing with another team this summer. Had such happened a real Kobepacalypse would have descended upon the city of angels and Lakers fans from L.A. to Taipei could be organizing an armed takeover of the Staples Center at this very moment.

While there are only three teams (the Chicago Bulls, Los Angeles Clippers and Phil Jackson's New York Knicks) that I believe Kobe would have *initially* considered signing with had the Lakers insulted him with an offer he deemed unfair, he would have had to take a massive, and I do mean massive, pay-cut to sign with any of those three teams. No matter how hard I try I just can't see that happening.

However, there is one team outside of Los Angeles that I do believe Kobe Bryant would have ultimately ended up signing with; a team that just so happens would have been thrilled to offer him a maximum contract as well. That team is Bryant's former hometown Philadelphia 76'ers.

The 76'ers may not have been able to offer the same title winning possibilities as the Bulls, let alone the Clippers, nor the familiarity of being led by Phil Jackson and the allure of playing in the basketball mecca that is NYC as the Knicks could have. However, the 76'ers could have offered Bryant and other-worldly amount of two things that no other team of interest could have: money and even more money in the future.

If Kobe Bryant believed it was unrealistic to think he would win another title to equal Michael Jordan's ring count, you better believe he would have loved to earn more in a single season than Jordan ever did and to therefore have the highest single season contract in NBA history. Only the Philadelphia 76'ers could realistically have offered such a contract.

Philadelphia is a title starved city. Their MLB Phillies have won just one World Series in the past 34 years and just two World Series in their 132 year history. Their NFL Eagles have never won a single Super Bowl. Their NHL Flyers haven't won a Stanley Cup in 40 years. And as for the 76'ers themselves, they have not won a single NBA title in the past 31 seasons! Philadelphia isn't just a title starved city but a city with one of the most tortured fan bases in sports history.

However, joy can come in many forms as any Allen Iverson fan knows. Signing Kobe Bean Bryant, the man who once starred for the *Aces* of Lower Merion High in Philadelphia's Main Line Suburbs would have brought a great deal of joy to the tortured Philly fans. And who knows, by his third year wearing the red, white and blue the young and talented 76'ers might just have won a ring of their own. Stranger things have happened, like Butler University making it to back to back NCAA Finals or A.C. remaining a virgin while balling for a title-winning Lakers squad in the 80s!

The largest single season salary in NBA history was Michael Jordan's 1997-98 salary of $33,140,000. Kobe Bryant's 2013-14 salary of $30,453,000 is the *second* largest. Coming *second* to Jordan in any category is not what Bryant strives for. However, the Philadelphia 76'ers could have offered Bryant the guaranteed largest single season contract in NBA history as part of a monstrous three year pact.

Philadelphia could easily have offered Kobe Bryant an absolute maximum $31,975,650 starting salary for the 2014-15 season which is a five percent raise from his previous year's salary. On top of this they could also have offered him 4.5 percent annual raises totaling $1,438,904.25 in the second and third years of a three year contract. This said Kobe's salaries under such a three year pact would have been as follows:

2014-2015:	$31,975,650
2015-2016:	$33,414,554.25
2016-2017:	$34,853,458.50 (highest ever)
Total Earnings:	$100,243,689.75

By the time the three-year mega-deal ended Kobe Bryant would not only have earned an NBA record $379,981,752 over the course of his career, absolutely dwarfing the second largest earner in NBA history by the name of Kevin Garnett (career-earnings of $315,373,398) by more than sixty-four million, he would also have dwarfed the career-earnings of former Lakers teammate and rival Shaquille O'Neal (career- earnings of $292,198,327) by more than eighty-seven million. And, it isn't beyond the realm of possibility to think that when the three-year mega-deal ended just before Bryant's 39th birthday, he actually could have signed another one or two year contract and became the first player to surpass the $400,000,000 career-earnings mark!

Not only could the Philadelphia 76'ers have offered Bryant the aforementioned three year, $100,243,690 contract, I actually believe they may have done so had the opportunity presented itself and the Lakers brass not avoided the

Kobepacalypse by inking him to the two year $48,500,000 contract they did! Think about that for a minute, seriously.

The 76'ers need a face of the franchise type superstar. They had Charles Barkley and the fans loved him but no titles came with *Sir Charles*. They had Allen Iverson as well but no titles came with The Answer either. Dr. J and Wilt Chamberlain were the greatest 76'ers ever and both stars brought just one title each to the *City of Brotherly Love*. Kobe Bryant could have done the same, especially with the help of Michael Carter-Williams, Nerlens Noel and whatever young stud(s) the 76'ers brass drafts this year (Note: The 76'ers not only have their own pick but own the rights to the Pelicans 2014' #1 pick as long as it's not in the Top 5 which it most likely won't be; they could therefore literally draft two future All-Stars such as Andrew Wiggins and Aaron Gordon) to go along with Carter-Williams, Noel, Thaddeus Young and Kobe Bryant himself!

Not only would Bryant, the man who led Philadelphia's moribund Lower Merion High School to a state championship in 1996 and who eclipsed the aforementioned Wilt Chamberlain's *Pennsylvania High School Career Scoring Record*, have been the perfect face of the franchise star for the 76'ers, his insanely high salary wouldn't even have been a major issue amazingly enough! The 76'ers could have easily fit a maximum contract, even one as large as Bryant's, into their salary cap space for the upcoming 2014-15 season, even had they received the rights to the Pelicans first round pick and it's the highest possible selection (which would be #6) as they could have simply waived Jason Richardson using the *stretch provision* and spread his remaining $6,601,125 salary out over the next three years with just $2,200,375 counting against the cap each year. That said, the 76'ers could have easily given Bryant the aforementioned maximum three-year $100,243,689.75 contract and still have fielded a top-six that would have looked as follows in 2014-15:

Point Guard:	Michael Carter-Williams
Shooting Guard:	Kobe Bryant

Small Forward: Andrew Wiggins

Power Forward: Aaron Gordon

Center: Nerlens Noel

6th Man: Thad Young

The above may not have been good enough or at least experienced enough to win a title in their first year together, especially as the bench would have been made up of mostly minimum contract players. However, I have little doubt that such a roster could have legitimately competed for a title within a few short years.

Another reason Kobe Bryant's mammoth maximum contract would not have been much of a financial issue for the 76'ers is due to the length and/or amount of their other star player's contracts. Both Michael Carter-Williams and Nerlens Noel would be on cheap rookie contracts for the life of Bryant's entire deal. Likewise any first-rounders the team was to draft would also be on cheap rookie contracts for the entire duration of Bryant's deal. In fact the only other player besides Bryant on the 76'ers roster that would have been due any significant amount of money whatsoever is Thad Young and his contract expires one year before Bryant's would.

A perfect storm of cap space, young talent already in place (Carter-Williams and Noel), high draft picks (both their own and the Pelicans this year) and Kobe Bryant's free agency could have swept into Philadelphia, stayed in Philadelphia and left Lakers fans in a suicidal rage. The Kobepacalypse could have ended with Kobe Bean Bryant wearing the red, white and blue of the Philadelphia 76'ers instead of the purple and gold of the Los Angeles Lakers. Thank God it didn't!

APPENDIX TWO:
An Open Letter to Phil Jackson

Dear Mr. Jackson,

Let me start by blowing the appropriate smoke. You are the greatest coach in the history of professional sports in my opinion and if there ever is a real NBA Mount Rushmore erected I believe you should be on it, along with either Kobe, Jordan and Magic or Kobe, Shaq and Jerry West, because really, why should any non-Lakers be allowed on such a monument anyways?

Please allow me to get right to the point. You left a great many Lakers fans heart-broken. Most, if not all Lakers fans, blame the Buss family instead of you for their heartache. However, it doesn't matter who is to blame, all that matters is the fans hearts have been broken.

I understand you're not coming back to the purple and gold. I understand you're in New York for the long-haul. All I ask is that you succeed and succeed wildly; for to leave the Lakers and do nothing more than tread water in New York and build a perennial playoff contender rather than an actual ring-winning team would be a slap in the face to Lakers fans everywhere.

All of the above said, the Knicks are horrible. Their roster is horrible. I can fix that for you. Just sit back, finish reading this letter, follow my plan and within 12 short months or so you could have another dynasty at your control.

I believe you know full well that the Knicks have no real shot at winning the title this coming season. This season needs to be a season of change, the season of trade, the season that initiates the re-birth of the Knicks franchise and makes it possible for a dynasty to arise in NYC when the 2015-16 season starts.

The first step in creating a new dynasty in the *Big Apple* is to clear the roster of as much dead-weight as possible. And, as the old saying goes, to get something good (in this case an enormous amount of cap space) you have to give up something good.

The one and only trade you need to make to start the dynasty process is as follows: The New York Knicks trade Carmelo Anthony, Raymond Felton, J.R. Smith and Pablo Prigioni to the Houston Rockets for Omer Asik, Jeremy Lin, Terrence Jones, Donatas Montiejunas and as many draft pics as you can pry out of Daryl Morey's hands as possible, if any.

Obviously the Rockets and GM Daryl Morey would never turn down the above offer as it would give them perhaps the most talented starting five in the history of the NBA with James Harden, Chandler Parsons, Carmelo Anthony, Dwight Howard and whoever they choose to start at the point guard position, be it the tough-as-nails, scrappy Patrick Beverly, the newly acquired Raymond Felton, or some guy named Porky McButter from the local Houston Y.M.C.A. Therefore Mr. Jackson, if *my deal* doesn't get done it will be on your head and I honestly believe that one day you will be sorry for not having heeded my advice.

In regards to your Knicks, while you may be able to receive a better single player from another team in trade than any one player in the aforementioned deal with Houston, the fact is that this trade swaps Carmelo Anthony and three players you would cut for nothing if you could just have the cap space back, for three legit starters and a talented young big, each with a coveted *expiring* contract! Your Knicks could easily make the playoffs this coming season in the weak Eastern Conference with a starting lineup of Jeremy Lin, Tim Hardaway Jr., Terrence Jones, Amar'e Stoudemire and Omer Asik.

However, this trade is not about the upcoming 2014-15 season, it's about creating a dynasty and rolling out the best roster in the league to start the 2015-16 season. The fact of the matter is that your Knicks would not have one single player with a guaranteed contract on the books for the 2015-16 season on their entire roster after completing this trade, not one single player!

If you wanted to Mr. Jackson, you could literally enter the summer of 2015 with over $65,000,000 in cap space to spend on such free agents as LeBron James, Rajon Rondo, LaMarcus Aldridge and Kevin Love amongst others. You would also have team options on young studs Tim Hardaway Jr. and Terrence Jones (as well Donatas Montiejunas who you may choose to let walk in order to save the cap space) that would only cost the team a total of $6,082,253 to pick up, as well as a $3,898,691 qualifying offer on the fine young perimeter defender Iman Shumpert.

The above said, if you follow *my plan* and complete the proposed trade with Daryl Morey in Houston you could enter the summer of 2015 with Shumpert, Hardway Jr., Jones and Montiejunas under contract and still have over $55,000,000 in cap space to spend, an amount that could be enough to sign LeBron James, Kevin Love and Rajon Rondo outright. You could even let Shumpert and Montiejunas walk and perhaps re-sign Omer Asik to a long-term contract using the $6,186,895 you saved.

If you follow my plan Mr. Jackson, your 2015-16 New York Knickerbockers starting lineup could feature Rajon Rondo, Tim Hardaway Jr., LeBron James, Kevin Love and Omer Asik ... and if that isn't a budding dynasty, I don't know what is and you can call me Otis Smith.

In conclusion; you're welcome Mr. Jackson. I look forward to receiving my consultation fee before the 2015-16 season tips off, as well as an invitation to the *Championship Parade* in the summer of 2016.

Sincerely,

Bryant T. Jordan

APPENDIX THREE:
LeBron James' New Decision

Many readers may wonder why LeBron James plays for the Cleveland Cavaliers and not the Miami Heat in this book. The answer to this question is two-fold.

Firstly, this is my book and if I want to write LeBron onto the Cavs rather than the Heat, onto the Cavs he shall go. Secondly, I honestly believe that if the Miami Heat do not three-peat as NBA Champions this season, there is a solid 55% chance LeBron will bolt South Beach and take his talents back to Cleveland – *at least we're not Detroit* – Ohio.

Would LeBron James really leave the shores of Biscayne Bay for the shores of the Cuyahoga River? Would he really trade the fun and sun of Miami for the snow, slush and sullenness of Cleveland? If such a trade would mean winning even one more ring over the remainder of his career, than I believe the answer is yes!

The man known as *King James* has a new decision to make this summer. However, he has already proven that he marches to the beat of his own drummer, that he does not care what his critics say, and that winning titles and increasing his personal legacy while building his individual brand are far more important to him than is loyalty to any one NBA franchise (and rightly so I might add).

James left Cleveland for Miami, not because Micky Arison was a better owner than Dan Gilbert or because Eric Spoelstra was a better coach than Mike Brown. He switched teams simply because he thought he could win more titles over the length of his next contract with the Heat than he could with the Cavs, period.

The above said, it stands to reason that this summer, when LeBron takes stock of his future and the probably futures of other teams around the league with him on their roster, he won't have a problem switching teams once again, if doing so will give him better odds at winning multiple titles. I personally believe joining the Cleveland Cavaliers would do just that.

Now, before I explain why leaving Miami for Cleveland makes too much sense for LeBron to ignore, I would like to touch on two apparent truths:

Firstly, I do believe if the Miami Heat three-peat this season, there is at least an 80 percent chance LeBron either picks up his *player option* or signs an extension and plays at least one more season with the Heat. Even if LeBron believes Wade is washed up and that Bosh is little more than a third option at this stage of his career when he truly needs a second option, I believe LeBron will return to Miami. I just cannot fathom how he could turn down the possibility, even if such is remote, of winning four-straight NBA titles with Miami, thereby accomplishing a feat Michael Jordan never did. LeBron wants to ascend to the top of the NBA's mythical Mount Rushmore and he knows that he needs to top Jordan, more so than any other single player, to do so.

Secondly, while most talking heads seem to feel the only team LeBron would even consider leaving the Heat for is the Cavaliers, I do believe that LeBron would consider other options if he felt such would help him win more titles than a move to Cleveland would bring. I also have no doubt in my mind that every single NBA team would willing move mountains to make it possible for LeBron to sign with them and that the only player in the entire league who's team would not trade him for LeBron, or to make room for LeBron, is 2013-14 NBA *MVP* Kevin Durant.

The above said, it would not shock me all that much to see LeBron James tell the Clippers he will ink a maximum contract with them, with a starting salary of $20,020,875 if they can open up a roster spot for him while at the same time keeping Chris Paul and Blake Griffin on the roster. However, as I don't believe the Miami Heat would agree to *trade* LeBron to another team and that they would in fact dare him to simply sign with another team, and as the trio of James, Paul and Griffin would be on the books for $57,722,126 all by themselves, leaving just $4,377,874 to spend on a minimum of nine other players which is less than even nine minimum contract salaries would account for, such is an impossibility, unless James decides to take a pay-cut and accept less than the maximum. I don't see that happening.

By the way, the above should tell the reader something, namely that many of the talking heads on sports shows around the country, have literally no idea what they are talking about when they talk about free agency signings and trades. During the 2013-14 season there was a report that Carmelo Anthony to the Clippers was a very realistic possibilty. When I heard that I laughed and knew that whoever first came up with such a ridiculous idea and whichever reports foolishly chose to report on such, each did so in complete ignorance and without any legitimate understanding of the salary cap, trade financial and the NBA's *Collective Bargaining Agreement.*

The simple fact is that due to Carmelo Anthony's previous contract with the Knicks being more lucrative than the previous contract LeBron James signed with the Heat, Anthony can earn a higher maximum salary than James this offseason. If it would be iimpossible for the Clippers to pair James with Chris Paul and Blake Griffin, it would be even more impossible for them to pair Anthony with the two Los Angeles stars. Simply put, take what you hear on sports broadcasts and news networks with a grain of salt, at least when it comes to free agency and trade rumors and gossip.

Back to LeBron and his new decision. While James may not be able to force his way to the Los Angeles Clippers or New York Knicks (who would need to find a team willing to absorb the contracts of both Amare Stoudemire and Andrea Bargnani if they wanted to team LeBron with Carmelo Anthony and a decent title-worthy roster), there is one team that I know James could join, would love to join, would love to have him join, and while such a team also may give James the greatest chance to win multiple titles, probably is an extreme long-shot. I am speaking of Kevin Durant's Oklahoma City Thunder!

I remember watching an NBA pre-game show with my son this season and Bill Simmons stating the Thunder would easily win the West if they would just trade Perkins and Lamb for the Orlando Magic's Aaron Afflalo. Now, don't get me wrong, I love The Sports Guy and think he's a genius writer and one of the best talking heads in the business, but his statement was just silly and akin to saying, *the Golden State Warriors would easily win the title if they would just trade Iggy and Barnes for LeBron* – of course they would, but it takes two teams to sign off on a trade – unless you're playing NBA2K.

The Magic would never agree to trade Afflalo for the horrendous *should have been amnestied* contract of Kendrick Perkins simply to land Jeremy Lamb; word is that they refused to swap Afflalo for Eric Bledsoe (who is in an entirely different stratosphere as a player than Jeremy Lamb) before the season started and if they did want to dump Afflalo they could get a whole lot more than Perkins and Lamb.

However, when Bill Simmons stated the Thunder needed to make a trade it got me thinking … what would have happened had Magic and Bird played together? What about Russell and Chamberlain? How about Shaq and Kobe; oh yeah, we know the answer to this last one, 3 NBA titles and 4 Conference championships in 5 years!

The above said, we all know LeBron had no problem signing with *Dwyane Wade's team* simply because he felt doing so gave him the greatest chance to win multiple rings. Of course he quickly turned the Heat into *LeBron's team* but the point is that he didn't mind signing with a team that already had a face of the franchise and beloved team leader. That said, what one player do you think LeBron feels could help him win the most rings possible? Kevin Durant of course!

If LeBron James tells the Thunder this summer, *I want to sign with you and play with K.D.,* not only will they move mountains to get him, they could actually do so very, very easily. Let me make this very clear, the Oklahoma City Thunder could easily make room to sign LeBron James to a max contract this summer, and, that hat is a horrifying thought for the rest of the NBA!

All the Thunder brass would need to do would be to trade the duo of Jeremy Lamb and Nick Collison for a future pick, which they could easily do, and trade Russell Westbrook for future picks as well, and obviously they would have no trouble doing that at all. There are probably upwards of 20 NBA franchises that would fall all over themselves to hand the Thunder first round draft picks from now through the next 6 years for Westbrook if they could.

Once the Thunder brass accomplished those two simple moves, they could pick up the team option on little-used but intriguing giant Hasheem Thabeet, sign five minimum level contract players and roll out the following title-ready roster to start the 2014-15 NBA season:

Starting Point Guard:	Reggie Jackson	$2,325,680
Starting Shooting Guard:	Kevin Durant	$19,997,513
Starting Small Forward:	LeBron James	$20,020,875
Starting Power Forward:	Serge Ibaka	$12,250,000
Starting Center:	Steven Adams	$2,184,960
Backup Point Guard:	Minimum Contract Player	
Backup Shooting Guard:	Minimum Contract Player	
Backup Small Forward:	Andre Roberson	$773,920
Backup Power Forward:	Perry Jones	$1,129,200
Backup Center:	Hasheem Thabeet	$1,250,000
11th Man:	Minimum Contract Player	
12th Man:	Minimum Contract Player	
13th Man:	Minimum Contract Player	

I don't know about you but that starting five would scare the pants off me, no matter which team I was in charge of! Now, I will say that I do not believe LeBron James will force his way to the Thunder, nor do I believe he would even seriously consider playing for the Thunder and with frenemy and arch-rival Kevin Durant ... unless ... both the Heat and Thunder fail to win the 2014 NBA title.

If the Heat win this season's title I believe LeBron will return to Miami for at least one more season. If the Thunder win the title I believe LeBron could bolt Miami, but not that he would join the current champion in Oklahoma. However, if a team like the Indiana Pacers or San Antonio Spurs win this year's title, I could most definitely see LeBron seriously considering teaming up with Kevin Durant in Oklahoma and forming the great dynasty the league has seen since the Bill Russell led Celtics!

Now, as *En Vogue*, and one of the most amazing looking women God ever created other than my wife, Cindy Herron, would say, *back to life, back to reality*.

It's now time to get back to explaining why leaving Miami for Cleveland makes too much sense for LeBron James to ignore:

The Miami Heat are cap-strapped, period. After Dwyane Wade, Chris Bosh and LeBron himself all exercise their player options for the 2014-15 season, those three salaries combined with nothing more than the inexpensive salaries of Chris *Birdman* Anderson and Norris Cole, place the Heat nearly $3,000,000 over the salary cap, with just five players under contract.

Just about the best thing the Miami brass can hope for is for all of their 2013-14 roster players to agree to re-sign, preferably at massive hometown discounts. Even if such happens, which is a long-shot, especially considering starting point guard Mario Chalmers may be looking for a sizeable raise and youngsters Michael Beasley and Greg Oden may desire to play for a team that will actually allow them to play the game of basketball outside of practice, the Heat will merely trot out a more aged and broken down version of their 2013-14 season. Such a roster certainly does not guarantee a title going forward and may not even be one of the four of five best rosters when the 2014-15 season rolls around.

However, over in Cleveland, the Cavs not only have a superstar point guard in Kyrie Irving. They have a 22 year old superstar point guard and a player that could be dominating the competition at a time when both Dwyane Wade and Chris Bosh are enjoying retirement. Irving, in and of himself, is reason enough for LeBron James to seriously consider a bolt back to Cleveland.

The Cavaliers also have 2013 #1 Draft Pick Anthony Bennett, a player who may have disappointed in his rookie season, but one with immense potential nonetheless, and yet another player that may be dominating the completion at a time when both Wade and Bosh are sipping drinks on a Miami Beach and enjoying their retirement. The 21 year old *tweener* actually had a very solid 10 game stint during the middle of his rookie season that started with his first career *double-double* and ended with a solid 15 point, 8 rebound performance. During the 10 games Bennett actually managed to average 16.5 points and

10.2 rebounds per 40 minutes while also knocking down seven three-pointers at a .412 clip, showing his potential as a dynamic *stretch-four* type of forward.

Cleveland also has a pair of #4 overall picks in 23 year old power forward Tristan Thompson and 22 year old shooting guard Dion Waiters. Both players are loaded with potential, and, just as with Irving and Bennett, could be starring in the league at a time when Dwyane Wade and Chris Bosh are playing NBA2K and wishing they were still in the league. Thompson is a double-double waiting to happen (career averages of close to 15 points and 12 rebounds per 40 minutes) while Waiters is a dynamic scorer (career average of nearly 21 points per 40 minutes) who was actually compared to Wade leading up to the 2012 NBA Draft.

The Cavs also have two other recently drafted youngsters on the books with cheap rookie scale contracts. Tyler Zeller, the 17th pick in the 2012 NBA Draft and a player with career per 40 minute averages of around 13 points, 9 rebounds and 1.4 blocks. And, Sergey Karasev, the 19th pick in the 2013 NBA Draft and a sweet shooting small forward from Russia.

Oh yeah, and they also won the Draft Lottery this past May 20th and have the number one overall pick in this June's upcoming draft as well. Whether they draft Joel Embiid, Andrew Wiggins or Jabari Parker, or simply trade the pick for an available superstar like Kevin Love, the simple fact is the Cavaliers are loaded, absolutely loaded!

The only other player Cleveland has *on the books* for the 2014-15 season is back-up point guard Jarrett Jack. Jack is a steady 30 year old combo guard, who despite having a bit of an off year this season, managed to average 9.6 points and 4.0 assists per game with a 2.35-to-1 assist-to-turnover ratio in just over 28 minutes per game.

The above said, if the Cavaliers were to sign LeBron James this summer to a maximum contract with a starting salary of $20,020,875 and draft and sign two rookies with their first and second round (via the Orlando Magic) draft picks, who for the sake of listing players in the following roster rather than just saying *Draft Pick,* I'll say Joel Embiid and Glenn Robinson III with the first and thirty-third overall picks, their roster would look as follows:

Starting Point Guard:	Kyrie Irving	$7,459,924
Starting Shooting Guard:	Dion Waiters	$4,062,000
Starting Small Forward:	LeBron James	$20,020,875
Starting Power Forward:	Trist. Thompson	$5,421,233
Starting Center:	Joel Embiid	$5,510,640
Backup Point Guard:	Jarrett Jack	$6,300,000
Backup Shooting Guard:	Sergey Karasev	$1,533,840
Backup Small Forward:	Anthony Bennett	$5,563,920
Backup Power Forward:	Free Agent – up to	$4,609,136
Backup Center:	Tyler Zeller	$1,703,760
11th Man:	Glenn Robinson	$507,336
12th Man:	Minimum Contract Player	

The ten players above would combine to earn $63,200,000 and therefore Cavaliers brass would indeed have up to $4,609,136 to spend on one free agent. This said, the team could sign one minimum player such as an undrafted rookie free agent like Iowa State's combo guard DeAndre Kane for example, and then use the remaining $4,609,136 to re-sign longtime Cavalier Anderson Varejao, whom they would have previously declined their team option on as he is no longer worth his scheduled salary. They could then sign one more minimum contract veteran, perhaps shooting guard and long-range bomber Anthony Morrow (if he chooses not to exercise his 2014-15 player option) and enter the 2014-15 season with the following roster:

Starting Point Guard: Kyrie Irving

Starting Shooting Guard: Dion Waiters

Starting Small Forward: LeBron James

Starting Power Forward: Tristan Thompson

Starting Center: Joel Embiid

Backup Point Guard: Jarrett Jack

Backup Shooting Guard: Anthony Morrow

Backup Small Forward: Anthony Bennett

Backup Power Forward: Anderson Varejao

Backup Center: Tyler Zeller

11th Man: Glenn Robinson

12th Man: Sergey Karasev

13th Man: DeAndre Kane

The Miami Heat simply cannot match, let alone top, the above lineup. They cannot legitimately surround LeBron with four 25 year old and under quality starters. They cannot surround LeBron with a roster that could realistically remain together and dominant for the next decade.

The Heat can offer LeBron an aged and experienced roster while the Cavs can offer LeBron a potential-laced roster filled with young stars. The Heat can offer LeBron a great shot at winning perhaps one more ring. The Cavs can offer LeBron a great shot at being in contention for a ring for the next 10 seasons.

I will say one final time. If the Heat win the 2013-14 title I do believe LeBron will play at least one more season in Miami. If they fail to do so I believe LeBron will seriously consider bolting to Cleveland. And, I for one, believe Cleveland offers LeBron a better chance at winning multiple rings over the next decade than Miami does, period.

PRINT BOOK BONUS APPENDIX

From: Bryant T. Jordan

Author of: *Saving the Lakers: A Be the General Manager Book*, *Saving the Celtics: A Be the General Manager Book* and *An Open Letter to ALL Regarding Donald Sterling*

Email: author@bryantTjordan.com

To: Cleveland Cavaliers General Manager David Griffin

Dear Mr. Griffin,

Please consider the following:

Cavaliers Trade:	2014 #1 Pick, Tristan Thompson, Anthony Bennett and Jarrett Jack
Raptors Trade:	Demar DeRozan, Jonas Valaciunas, 2014 #20 pick and the expiring contract of Dwight Buycks

Why the Raptors Agree:

Andrew Wiggins belongs on the Toronto Raptors, to play his entire career with the Raptors, to retire a Raptor and to be the first (and perhaps only) player to have his jersey hanging from the rafters and number retired. That the Raptors would also be acquiring talented and potential-filled *Canadians* in Anthony Bennett and Tristan Thompson – both of which are players that I believe would not only agree to contract extensions down the line but actually desire to sign such extensions with the Raptors more so than with any other team in the league – is a great plus as well; a great plus that Raptors General Manager Masai Ujiri should appreciate a great deal.

I sincerely believe that Andrew Wiggins, Tristan Thompson and Anthony Bennett will not only be ecstatic to be traded to the Toronto Raptors, but that they will be ecstatic to stay with the Raptors for the remainder of their careers. And, as I also believe that all three will most likely be playing for the *Canadian Olympic Team* in the 2016, 2020, 2024 Olympics and on, the chemistry of a team lead by such players could be San Antonio Spurs-esque.

In regards to Jarrett Jack, he is a quality backup combo guard and if the Raptors happen to lose Kyle Lowry to free agency, Jack would be a capable veteran starter on a young team lead by *The Canadian Three* of Wiggins, Thompson and

Bennett, along with talented swingman Terrence Ross. And, if Lowry happens to re-sign with the Raptors, Jack would be a great first guard off the bench.

The above said, I believe my trade proposal is not only a no-brainer trade for the Toronto Raptors franchise, the Raptors faithful fans, the city of Toronto, the Province of Ontario and for Canada as a country; I believe it's a no-brainer trade for General Manager Masai Ujiri as well. He can cement his place in Canadian lore by pulling off this trade and that is why YOU Mr. Griffin, need to strike while the iron's hot, and pull off this deal NOW!

Why the Cavaliers Agree:

I believe you're intelligent enough to recognize my trade proposal as a no-brainer, in the same way I believe Lakers General Manager Mitch Kupchak was intelligent enough to recognize my January, 2008 trade proposal of Kwame Brown, Javaris Crittenton, Marc Gasol, picks and cash for Pau Gasol; a trade (with the addition of Aaron Mckie) that Kupchak did in fact pull off, and which led to the Lakers 3-peating as Western Conference champions and winning two more NBA titles as well. However, please indulge me and allow me to write my piece.

I recognize that one of the most difficult aspects of being the General Manager of the Cleveland Cavaliers and building a perennial title-contender in Cleveland is the stigma that Cleveland is a small – and cold – market. It's one thing to draft a star prospect or even trade for a star talent, and yet an entirely different thing to keep such a talent locked up for the long-term. The tortured Cleveland fans know this better than anyone. That said, I believe you have one of the most difficult jobs in the league as you not only have to build a title-contender, you have to do so in a market that many players don't respect or appreciate. For example, you may be able to offer a wonderful trade package for a star player such as Kevin Love, only to watch him play for nothing more than his next contract, and then bolt Cleveland as soon as the 2014-15 season ends, in order to sign with a big market team like the Lakers or Knicks – even if LeBron

James does actually sign with the Cavaliers this summer. Kevin Love seems to have stars in his eyes and *winning* may not cure his wanderlust.

I also realize that LeBron James may not be ready to rejoin the Cavaliers with the current roster being what it is – even if a young star center like Joel Embiid is added to the mix. LaMarcus Aldridge isn't available. And, as for Kevin Love, I've explained my thoughts on him already.

However, the Toronto Raptors are ripe for the picking! There fan base is head over heels with Andrew Wiggins and Canadian *We are the North* pride is in full swing. If the fans get wind that the Cleveland Cavaliers have offered to trade the number one pick – and therefore their beloved Andrew Wiggins – along with two more young and talented Canadian players in Tristan Thompson and Anthony Bennett, they will be over the moon with excitement and demanding such a trade be completed. If Raptors General Manager Masai Ujiri does not pull the trigger on such a trade offer, the fans could be calling for his head – or at least his resignation since Canadians aren't as big on violence as Americans are – and demanding *Maple Leaf Sports and Entertainment* pull the trigger on the trade themselves.

As for the players themselves: DeMar DeRozan is a bona fide All-Star, just 24 years old and coming off a year where he was the 9th leading scorer in the NBA. However, as good as DeRozan is, Jonas Valanciunas may turn out to be even better. The big Lithuanian is just 22 years old and coming off a season in which he averaged 11 points and 9 boards and then upped his game in the playoffs by averaging 11 points and 10 boards while shooting over 63% from the field!

As for the #20 pick, it is also more valuable than ever this year, as the current draft crop is thought to be the deepest the league has seen since 1996 – at least that is my personal opinion - regardless of what the generally ingenious Jerry West thinks on the matter. As for the inclusion of the little-used Dwight Buycks, he is nothing more than a throw-in to *make financials work* of course.

When this deal and the NBA Draft is concluded, the Cavaliers will have just nine players *on the books*, including starters: Kyrie Irving, Dion Waiters, DeMar DeRozan, Jonas Valanciunas, and reserves: Tyler Zeller, Sergey Karasez, Dwight Buycks and whatever player they draft with the #20 pick (let's say Michigan State University power forward Adreian Payne) and the #33 pick (let's say Witchita State University swingman Cleyanthony Early) – and – the team will have also have $32,479,938 in available cap space. That's right, thirty-two million four hundred and seventy-nine thousand nine hundred and thirty-eight dollars in cap space!

With the aforementioned $32,479,938 in cap space your Cavaliers could literally offer LeBron James a maximum contract with a starting salary of $20,020,875, add one minimum contract veteran (let's say veteran point guard Devin Harris) to the roster, and still have $11,951,727 to spend on just one more starting big-man, while also being able to move Dion Waiters to the 6th man spot. With that $11,951,727 the Cavaliers could easily sign a big like Pau Gasol, Marcin Gortat or perhaps even Zach Randolph if the Grizzlies amnesty him, along with another quality free agent.

However, I personally believe if the Cavaliers *threw the house* – meaning all $11,951,727 of their remaining cap space – at the Detroit Pistons restricted free agent Greg Monroe in the form of a 4 year $51,033,874 contract, the Pistons may not match such a lucrative offer, and your Cavaliers could add one of the best young big men in the league to an already insanely potent roster. Such moves would give them a truly dynastic roster moving forward, a roster that would look as follows:

PG:	Kyrie Irving
SG:	DeMar DeRozan
SF:	LeBron James
PF:	Greg Monroe
C:	Jonas Valanciunas
PG:	Devin Harris

SG:	Dion Waiters
SF:	Cleanthony Early
PF:	Adreian Payne
C:	Tyler Zeller
11th Man:	Sergey Karasez
12th Man:	Dwight Buycks

Honestly, if LeBron James would rather play with the aging Dwyane Wade and Chris Bosh than with Kyrie Irving, DeMar DeRozan, Jonas Valanciunas *and* Greg Monroe, many will believe he is certifiably insane and ready for a padded room. LeBron James could literally own the NBA for the next decade playing with the above roster, a roster you would have built! By the time James' career winds down, he may not be chasing Michael Jordan's ring count, but Bill Russell's instead!

Now, just for the sake of argument – even if LeBron James doesn't return to Cleveland this summer (and if the Heat 3-Peat I don't think he will return to Cleveland, at least not before the 2015-16 season) and the Pistons decide to match the aforementioned 4 year $51,033,874 offer on Greg Monroe – your Cavaliers could still build a vastly improved roster by signing Carmelo Anthony in place of James, as well as the duo of Pau Gasol, and say, Andray Blatche in place of Greg Monroe, while also drafting point guard Elfrid Payton instead of power forward Adreian Payne with their #20 pick, and signing a veteran big like Emeka Okafor instead of Devin Harris to a minimum contract. Such moves would give the team the following roster to start next season:

PG:	Kyrie Irving
SG:	DeMar DeRozan
SF:	Carmelo Anthony
PF:	Pau Gasol
C:	Jonas Valanciunas

PG:	Elfrid Payton
SG:	Dion Waiters
SF:	Cleanthony Early
PF:	Andray Blatche
C:	Tyler Zeller
11th Man:	Emeka Okafor
12th Man:	Sergey Karasez
13th Man:	Dwight Buycks

The above roster is good enough to compete for a title immediately. More importantly, the above roster may be more than enough to lead tortured Cavaliers fans to consider you, David Griffin, a miracle worker, period. And, being considered a miracle worker can't be bad for an NBA General Manager these days.

Mr. Griffin, I believe if you contact Masai Ujiri, explain all of the above to him in your own words and work the ole *Griffin-magic*, you will be able to convince him to agree to such a trade and will be responsible for building the greatest roster in Cleveland Cavaliers history. In short, I believe you will be a legend!

Oh, and by the way, I won't even charge you a consulting fee. Just put me on the payroll after the Cavaliers win their first tilte, give me a massive cash bonus after they repeat and give me a lifetime consultant position after the 3-Peat.

Sincerely,

Bryant T. Jordan

ABOUT THE AUTHOR

Bryant T. Jordan is the author of *Saving the Lakers: A Be the General Manager Book* and *Saving the Celtics: A Be the General Manager Book.* He has been a freelance writer for over 15 years.

BTJ as many know him lives in a rural paradise with his high-school sweetheart and wife of 17 plus years, as well as his magnificent children, under the amazing care of His God and Savior. He considers himself the most blessed man on the planet, period.

You can generally find him leaving thought-proving tweets on Twitter @bryantTjordan

www.BryantTJordan.com

Printed in Great Britain
by Amazon